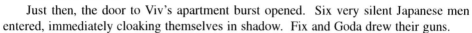

"Jason— The green light— T
just like he said!"

"Look, you can't tell anybody ab..... ...

"The Hell I can't!"

Just then, the door to Viv's apartment burst opened. Six very silent Japanese men
entered, immediately cloaking themselves in shadow. Fix and Goda drew their guns.

"Where is Victor?" said the leader impatiently.

"Drop your weapons, I'm a cop."

"You did not answer my question."

"Uh, Goda, I don't think these— Gggg! Akkkk!"

Dropping his gun, Mark dropped to his knees, choking and grasping his throat. The
Stuff had one more power to imbue upon him. Goda picked up Mark's gun and tried in
vain to keep all the Japanese guys in his line of sight.

"You picked the wrong time to swallow a bug, Fix."

"By the time we are finished with you two," added the Japanese leader. "Neither one
of you will be able to swallow much of anything. Now, where is Victor?!"

"Goda," gasped Fix. "Grab...onto...something."

"What?"

Mark couldn't hold back any longer. A roar that shatter Viv's windows and shook
everyone else's for blocks, rocked the yuppie apartment complex. Strange bolts of green
energy erupted from Mark's body, instantly burning holes through his clothes and bouncing around the room like mini balls of lightning. The clocks, lights and appliances went
berserk. Viv's stereo surged to life, it's volume controls rolling to maximum and blasting
"Rock N' Roll is Dead" by Lenny Kravitz. Fog billowed in the room from out of nowhere,
but was blown away by a powerful surge of wind that impossibly emanated from Mark's
windpipe.

Goda stamped his foot, locking the magnet against the base of the balcony's sliding
door just in time. Two of the Japanese men were blown off the balcony, while the others
were tossed about the room. When the wind subsided, Goda made his move. Grabbing
Mark by the collar, he dragged the spent P.I. to his feet and they both stumbled out of the
apartment.

"How did you do that?" asked Goda as he stumbled.

"If I knew that, I'd sell my gun," gasped Mark. "You got a breath mint?"

THE FIX:®

FIX IN OVERTIME

To Brian
Fix was here.

written & created by

Tony DiGerolamo

illustrated by

Brendon Fraim & Brian Fraim

PADWOLF
PUBLISHING

PADWOLF PUBLISHING INC.
457 Main Street, #384
Farmingdale, NY 11735

www.padwolf.com

Art Team
Penciled & Lettered by Brendon Fraim
Inks & Grey Tones by Brian Fraim

Back Cover Photo of Mark Tommy Frkovich
Computer Enhancements Mammon Graphics, Ltd.

Book Edited and Copy Edited by Deborah Wunder.

ISBN: 1-890096-09-1

Printed in the USA

First Printing.

Special thanks to Russ Murray, Don Hutter, John Vitti, Dave Juskow, Ben Plavin, Chris Welsh, Mike Ewing, Daylin Leach, The Next Line Comedy Theater, Pat, Marie, Diane, Deb, Neil, Beth, Elizabeth & The Beastie Boys.

A big thank you to Brian and Bredon Fraim, who have been there since the beginning in 1995. Thanks for all your hard work guys. Fix has never looked better.

Dedicated to my folks, even though mom hates the back cover picture. Thanks to them and all of my family for their love and support over the years.

THE TALLY-HO ARCADE IS NESTLED IN A DECAYING 80'S SHOPPING PLAZA RIGHT NEXT TO MY OFFICE. IT'S THE SORT OF SAD, "WHY DID THEY BOTHER?" KIND OF PLACE, WHERE THE LOCAL SKATE PUNKS BIDE THEIR TIME, WAITING FOR IT TO CLOSE FOR GOOD, SO THE PARKING LOT WILL FINALLY BE COMPLETELY CAR FREE.

MY OFFICE, WHICH IS CURRENTLY CLIENT FREE, IS IN DESPERATE NEED OF CLEANING AND I MADE THE MISTAKE OF ASKING MINDY TO HELP ME.

MINDY IS (FOR LACK OF A BETTER TERM TO DESCRIBE WHAT LAUGHINGLY PASSES FOR OUR RELATIONSHIP) MY GIRLFRIEND. DON'T ASK ME TO EXPLAIN THE WHY'S AND HOW'S, YOU DON'T HAVE THAT KIND OF TIME. SUFFICE IT TO SAY, MINDY'S PERSONAL SOUND-TRACK IS JANET JACKSON'S "WHAT HAVE YOU DONE FOR ME LATELY?" AND MINE IS JOHN COUGAR'S "I NEED A LOVER THAT WON'T DRIVE ME CRAZY".

AS FOR ME, I'M JUST HOPING I CAN TALK MINDY INTO BED LATER OR AT LEAST GET OUT OF HERE WITHOUT STARTING AN ARGUMENT. MY NAME'S MARK MAMMON. MINDY CALLS ME SHITHEAD. YOU CAN CALL ME FIX.

YOUR CLIENTS ARE PIGS.

I'M THE PIG. I POUR THE COFFEE FOR THEM.

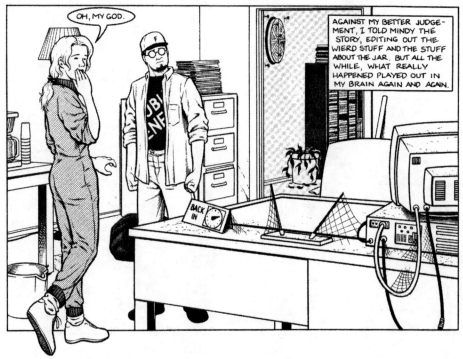

BUT I COULDN'T BELIEVE THAT.

I WOULDN'T BELIEVE THAT.

I TOOK SOME OF THE STUFF. I'D EXPLAIN IT TO YOU, BUT, AGAIN, YOU DON'T HAVE THAT KIND OF TIME.

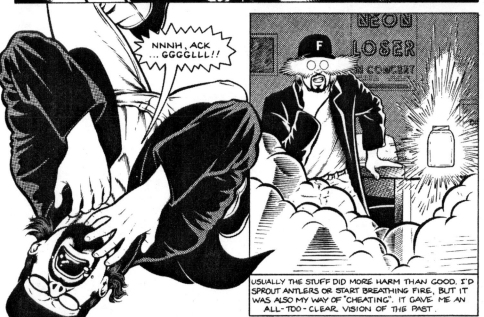

NNNH, ACK ...GGGGLLL!!

USUALLY THE STUFF DID MORE HARM THAN GOOD. I'D SPROUT ANTLERS OR START BREATHING FIRE, BUT IT WAS ALSO MY WAY OF "CHEATING". IT GAVE ME AN ALL-TOO-CLEAR VISION OF THE PAST.

GHOSTLY IMAGES OF CLAREESE AND GORDO PLAYED OUT IN FRONT OF ME.

SHE PLAYED HIM FOR A SUCKER.

WHICH MAKES IT EVEN WORSE.

I FOLLOW THE VISION TO A STORAGE FACILITY IN DEPTFORD. THE STUFF WEARS OFF, BUT I KNOW I'M CLOSE.

NOW I SIT IN SILENCE, STARING AT AN EMPTY RECEPTIONIST'S DESK, WHILE MINDY TRIES TO MAKE UP FOR WRENCHING THE STORY OUT OF ME.

I THINK ABOUT GORDO AND THE FUTURE. SOMEDAY, I'M GONNA WRITE MY AUTOBIOGRAPHY. CHAPTER 3 WILL BE ALL ABOUT GORDO AND MY FINAL SHOWDOWN WITH CLAREESE THE SECRETARY.

AND EVERYBODY WILL READ THAT I LET HER GO AND SHE DISAPPEARED IN AN EXPLOSION OF NOISE AND LIGHT.

THE END.

PROLOGUE:

The initiation was simple. All Kai had to do was walk right up to a total stranger and blow his brains out with the .38 his brother, Hwan, had given to him. There was no conscience to wrestle with, since Kai would not know this person. It would be over in an instant, like a bad dream; gone from memory as soon as he rounded the corner and dropped the gun in a sewer.

The gang was known as the Arikas, their copyright infringement against the popular Japanese comic book just another entry in their long list of crimes. Most of them had records before they were 16 and would never leave the Yakuza minors. But Kai was different, — Smart like his brother. Soon, he too would be honored with tattoos and rewarded with fast cars and beautiful women.

Kai immediately recognized the man pushing the shopping cart from the night before. A tall, muscular homeless man, who eluded his gun when Philly's Finest happened by unexpectedly. Kai had cleverly dropped the gun in a trashcan, then came back for it later. He took the reappearance of the bum as an omen that he should kill him.

He approached quietly, from behind, without speaking. There was no honor in prolonging it; after all, this was just business, nothing personal. Kai approached, jammed the barrel solidly against the back of his head and squeezed the trigger.

Pop!

The bum's head exploded, like an overripe watermelon, spraying Kai unexpectedly. "Damn!" thought Kai. "I angled the gun too high. Very unprofessional. Very unprofessional."

But that was the least of Kai's worries, for as he cleared the blood from his eyes, he noticed a sort of slurping sound. When he looked up, the bum was still standing. The bloody stump of a neck had sealed itself and quickly began forming a new head from the green-black flesh inside the bum's torso. Kai watched in morbid fascination. Unafraid, he prepared to fire again.

"Are you Kai Ikashi?" asked the bum's mouth as it formed.

"Yes," answered Kai, amused. "How do you know my name, dead man?"

"Oh," smiled the bum, raising his arms, which now ended in two-foot long jagged knives. "I'm not the dead man."

The bum moved so fast, Kai blinked and missed it, but not before he fired his gun. It hit the bum in the arm, nearly shearing it off. Kai's gun ended up on the sidewalk, along with his right hand and wrist.

Kai clutched his bloody stump, his mouth screaming in pain and surprise. Some primal instinct drove Kai's feet away from the suddenly terrifying homeless man.

The bum paused momentarily, letting his blood and flesh run back into his arm and torso. Then he pulled a small boom box from his shopping cart. He began to play a CD. It was *Possum Kingdom* by the Toadies. He also stopped to get Kai's gun, since it was there. The bum took his time. Kai wouldn't get far.

Following Kai's trail of blood, the bum tracked him past rows of abandoned buildings. He'd be heading for the lights near Vine Street, but he'd never get there. The bum turned up the boom box, letting the lead singer of the Toadies scream, "Do you want to die?" It echoed through the dark, empty streets, instilling the shadows with additional eeriness.

Kai was feeling lightheaded. Staggering towards Vine Street, he spotted the familiar landmarks of Chinatown. Maybe his brother would send someone back for his hand. They could reattach it. But how would he explain the bum?

Then, suddenly, the bum turned the corner in front of him. The music was blaring and almost distracted Kai enough from seeing the bum aim the .38. Kai dove through a partially boarded up window, then scrambled for the shadows.

He was in an old church. It would provide him with plenty of cover, if he could just stay conscious long enough. Taking the .22 from the ankle holster on his right leg, he thrust the gun towards the darkness. But the bum was already inside, stepping out of a much closer shadow than Kai anticipated. He fired like a panicked tourist into the bum's torso, hitting him with every shot. The bum wavered, looked down at the holes, than raised the .38 toward Kai's head.

Then, it hit him. Kai recognized the bum. It was insane, but he was no bum at all. Incomprehensibly, he saw him as he stepped into a slice of light, which fell from a street lamp outside. At the same time, he knew, with the clarity of a dying man, that this was no fake, no imitator, no coincidence of genetics. The man about to shoot looked exactly like one of the most famous faces in football, the ex-quarterback, now Channel 12 sportscaster, Sammy Arnski. And not only that, it was a younger, robust Arnski, with a full head of blonde hair, like he had during his Super Bowl wins in the 70's. But his eyes were unreal looking — Pupilless, steely and as silver as mercury. He focused on Kai with a cold, determined meanness and placed the barrel against his forehead.

"If one of us lives," intoned Sammy somberly. "We all live."

Pop!

<u>CHAPTER 1</u> (Mark): Abrasion Mountain

I knew exactly how guilty O.J. was, which is why I never could stomach the trial proceedings on CNN. I had folded back the canvas, seen the wizard behind Oz, knew what could not be known, but I couldn't do a damn thing about it. That's the real bitch about occasional omnipotence; it leaves you wanting more. Like a Yum's potato chip or only getting to second base.

Not that I'm complaining, mind you. Hell, I'd have a whole lot less reason to smile in the morning if it hadn't been for the Stuff, but that's another story. Right now I'm in the middle of the Shit...again.

Later on, I'd tell the story as if I loved it. There I was dodging bullets on the grounds of the abandoned Water Action Amusement Park in Pine Hill, New Jersey. Was this Act III of a 70's TV police drama, or what? The owner of the bullets included Jason Porter and a couple of drug runners with Jamaican accents and Uzi attitudes. Jason's wife had hired me to find out if he was cheating on her.

Turns out Jason's a good husband, but a real lousy cop. He'd been using his police connections to set up drug deals. The Stuff told me he'd be here, but I was expecting a scantily clad coat check girl, not the Jamaican Uzi patrol. I busted into their meeting at an abandoned go-kart garage armed with nothing but my mother's camera and half a roll of film. You should've seen their faces. (Actually, you can, I took a picture.) After blinding them with the flash, I grabbed an important-looking briefcase and got my ass out of there. Picked the cocaine tote bag on the first try. I got stupid luck that way, although my friends just call me stupid for short. You can call me Fix.

"Fix!" Porter screamed across the ruined park. How Porter could figure out my nickname from the "F" on my baseball cap was beyond me. I dressed like one of the locals — Hell, I *am* a local. Jeans, sneakers, steel rimmed glasses and a concert shirt for a local band called The Wondrous Crappers. My goatee gave me that "fresh out of college" look that policemen just can't stand. But I generally try and keep a low profile, so it was odd that Porter knew me.

"Just give us back the briefcase and you can walk out of here!"

Yeah, *that* sounded sincere. After a failed arson attempt and several years of lax maintenance, the woods had reclaimed enough of the park to provide me with adequate cover to
keep Porter frustrated. I was hiding near the crumbling remains of ticket booth for the
formula one racing cars.

"Watchu think you're doin'?" one of the Jamaicans complained. "You know this
mon'?"

"He's a private detective. Lucky as shit."

Jeez, I never get any credit.

"Circle around and cut him off. Don't fire unless you see him. I can't cover for us
unless he's dead."

Earlier, I had taken off my overcoat and gun and left them in the parking lot of a
nearby apartment complex. Despite this rather sorry state of affairs, I had three things
going for me; 1) as soon as one of these guys fired, someone would call the police; 2) as a
youth, I worked at the park and knew every inch, and; 3) I still had half a vial of the Stuff
in my pocket. As I crept my way through some underbrush, past a sign that says, "You
have to be this high to ride the bumper boats", I really regretted not bringing my disc
player. Sneaking around guys in dreads and funky knit hats just screamed for a little
Ska'.

"What the fuck are you doin'?" Ska-boy #1 said to #2.

Ska-boy #2 coughed up something and spat. He sounded like he had the flu, which
meant he'd want to kill me and get home to bed that much quicker.

"I'm climbin' above, so's to see him. Just search the fuckin' grounds, mon'."

Ska-boy #2 was climbing the charred remains of the Zoom Tubes. The Zoom Tubes,
which I called the "Death Tubes" when I worked here, consisted of lengths of twisted
sewer pipes that would accommodate the urban suckers who wanted to wait in line 30
minutes, shoot down a water tube for ten seconds, then belly flop into a pool that was kept
at a perpetual 69 degrees, so the owner could admire the pert young nipples that frolicked
in his artificial surf. Anyone over two-hundred pounds that rode it, shook the whole
platform when they slid down the tubes. This whole stupid park was put together with a
Phillips screwdriver and a wrench. I wouldn't go on the Zoom Tubes when they were
running the stupid thing. One fat fuck nearly collapsed it on half the park. Now this guy,
who had the flu, was climbing it years later, after someone had already tried to burn it
down once. *And* he was cradling an Uzi with the safety off. A Bob Sagett video in the
making.

I had made my way to the old bumper boat pool, which still held the algae-covered
remains of two bumper boats. It was amazing that algae even grew in this water. The
guys who fixed the boats routinely spilled gasoline in it. Ska-boy #2 looked down just in
time to see the suitcase I grabbed float to the middle of the pool and begin to sink in its
murky waters.

"He threw it in the pool! Get your lazy butt over dere and retrieve it!"

Ska-boy #2 continued to call for Porter, who was looking for me somewhere near the
park entrance. Ska-boy #1 got to the edge of the pool and nearly retched. That bumper
boat water was *nasty*.

"How you expect me to go in this green, slimy water, then? I'll ruin my good jeans,
mon'."

The suitcase continued to bubble and sink.

"Just get yo' ass in there, fo' it ruin da coke!"

It was like being chased by Bob Marley's relatives.

"No good, slimy, pool shit," muttered Ska-boy #1, as he slid in. I remembered the same feeling myself when I had to slide into the water to assist a wounded 12-year-old. The pool had a cement bottom, yet your feet always felt something smooth and squishy on the bottom.

"Dis is disgustin', mon!"

"Hurry up!"

And, of course, if you were fixing a boat and dropped a tool or a spent spark plug or something sharp and metal, it was conveniently forgotten about.

"Ah! Shit! I kill dis Fix," muttered #1.

With the mention of my name, I popped up from behind the edge of the pool. Ska-boy #1 was shoulder deep in the watery slime, trying to pull the briefcase off the bottom of the pool.

"Hello. I really don't care about your drug deal. I mean, my girlfriend's got a pharmacy running through her veins. I'd just as soon—"

Ska-boy #1 raised his Uzi, I jumped for cover screaming, "I wouldn't do that!"

Ska-boy #1 let the bullets fly, riddling a nearby bumper boat and igniting the half-gallon of fuel left in its tank. This, of course, ignited the mixture of gas and oil which was floating on the pool from the second boat, which I sabotaged just a few seconds earlier. Ska-boy #1 flailed incoherently, screaming through the jacket of flame that enveloped him. He was determined to put out the fire without ducking into the water.

"Porter! Want to be gettin' over here?"

Ska-boy #2 was too far away to be very accurate with an Uzi, but he was anxious to shoot me. He shifted along the length of the Zoom Tubes platform, oblivious to its condition, until the vibrations from the kickback shook a support and sent the whole thing crashing into an empty pool 30 feet below. There was a nice, meaty-sounding crack, as he landed back first on the wooden debris below.

Porter was scrambling through the debris which was once the first aid station. (And, as the employees used to say, "The busiest ride in the park".) I was trying to scramble up the hill and into some thicker woods, but Porter spotted me. Fortunately, the fire from the boats was between him and me and it served to obscure his infrared targeting sensors. Oh, yeah, I forgot to mention. Porter's a cyber-cop. Should I start the story over?

"I know where you live, Fix!" huffed Porter, trying to get around the fire. "Don't make me run!"

Make *him* run? At this point, my heart was just about ready to explode. I guess 29 years of Castle Burgers and éclairs can have an adverse effect on your jogging performance. Trying not to wheeze, I stumbled up a partially foam-covered hill with weeds growing out of it. It had once been a waterslide the employees called "Abrasion Mountain," due to the frequent accidents. Most involved overzealous teenagers getting a running start and a ride supervisor who routinely abandoned his post to make out with the girl from the formula one ticket booth. I think me and Porter were having more fun in the park now than the customers did when it was open.

"Fix, please!" pleaded Porter, as he crested the hill near the inner tube slide. "That money wasn't for me, it was for my kids! You have any kids, Fix? Do you know what its like?"

That lying bastard. His wife told me he just bought a boat.

"There's gonna be cops here any minute. Who do you think they're going to believe?"

Porter's cybernetics finally adjusted to the heat. He could clearly see my heat trail leading all the way up to a tree draped in deflated inner tubes. He started firing and I crouched down behind the tree. Porter's gun tore the sides to splinters, and I could feel some of the bullets whiz over my head as they penetrated the wood. I was reaching in my pocket for the half vial of Stuff, when I heard his gun wheeze and lock up.

While Porter fumbled to unjam, I charged out at him from behind the tree. His cybernetics, courtesy of the Philadelphia Police Department, were highly sophisticated, but highly temperamental. If he stuck with short bursts, it wouldn't have happened. The only reason Porter got the cybernetics was because, at the time, the only people eligible to get them were police officers injured in the line of duty. Never mind the fact that 40% of the injuries were accidents on the job, by chuckleheads like Porter, who never should've been issued a uniform to begin with. A combination of budget cuts and lawsuits stemming from cybernetic medical complications shut the program down last year. One of the suits alleged that the metal implants required made the recipient top heavy, which is why Porter keeled over so easily. We both tumbled down the dry, foam banks of the inner tube ride.

"Ow! Man!" The weight of Porter's right arm became apparent. "Get off! Get off!"

The inner tube ride was called "River County" or "Rapids County" or something. It was the most popular ride to work, since customers frequently lost jewelry, cash and other belongings as they slid down the ride. (Nearly caught a wallet once, myself.) As Porter and I bounced and slid, extra bullets fell out of his pockets, while mom's camera, my wallet, car keys and change decided to enjoy the ride separately.

"This was— Ow! —more fun with— Ow! —water," I muttered, bouncing over tattered bumps of brown foam.

Porter's gun was connected to his arm by a thin filament of metal, that went from his wrist to the handle of the pistol. The filament suddenly retracted and the gun shot back into his hand.

"Wait a minute!" I pleaded. "Your wife sent me!"

"How do you know Karen?" Porter demanded.

Porter hesitated and failed to notice a rusty steel spike on the next turn. When the maintenance guys had to fix the foam on these rides, they frequently used three-foot-long construction spikes to hold the foam back while they worked underneath. One time, they forgot a spike and one of the customers tore his kneecap off. I guess when the park went belly-up the maintenance guys left a lot of spikes behind. Porter's filament got caught on one during a turn, holding the gun fast. Unfortunately, Porter continued to slide and the filament snapped. Considering that the filament was anchored to one of the bones in his arm and considering the howl he let out when it snapped back in his face, I'd say I was pretty well fucked if I didn't get off this ride.

"Karen thought you were cheating on her," I gritted, trying to get a grip on the crumbling foam.

Using my momentum, I attempted to roll off the ride in a spot that occasionally threw customers off into the woods. Unfortunately, without the water, I wasn't high enough to get out. I grabbed the edge, but as Porter slid by he locked onto my leg with a dime store, kung-fu grip. The foam edge I was clutching immediately gave way and we continued our journey toward an empty pool 30 or so feet away.

"I never cheated on her! You tell her that!" Porter ordered, suddenly shifting his priorities.

Blood streamed down Porter's face as he attempted to crush my leg. I let out a yelp, then tried to reach for Porter's gun, which was just above, bouncing down the chute at a slower speed, along with the half a vial of Stuff.

"Owww! Leggo, asswipe!"

I gave Porter a couple of swift kicks in the chops and then we got to the end of the ride. Now, during the park's operation, riders could look forward to a refreshing splash in the bottom wading pool, with water which was being continuously pumped to the top of the hill from a nearby pumping station. The pumping station itself of little more than a fence, a pump and a 20 foot deep reserve of stagnant water and lost bikini tops. Unfortunately, the owner of the park owned other, more successful parks, so the pumping station, fence and wading pool had been ripped out. Porter and I crash landed into an empty hole full of leaves, rusty spikes and foam debris.

Porter immediately got to his feet, while I was still trying to steady myself against the side of the empty pool. With his cybernetically- enhanced arm, he pushed me up against the wall and held me by the throat.

"Who said I was cheating on Karen?" he demanded. "Who?!"

"Let go of me and I'll—"

Porter tightened his grip and lifted me off my feet.

"Karen sent me," I gasped.

"Why?!"

"She said you were— Ack!"

I saw the vial stop on the ledge about above us. I could see the glowing, green goo contained therein. It teetered on a piece of foam two feet beyond my reach. Porter set me back on my feet so he could loosen his grip and so I could finish my sentence.

"She said you were getting strange phone calls and leaving at all hours of the night."

I punctuated this revelation by kicking him in the groin. Furious, Porter grabbed me and lifted me higher, but threw me aside before I could reach the vial. Porter's gun fell on the ground nearby and he picked it up.

"If you shoot me," I tried to reason. "I can't go back and tell Karen how faithful you are."

A few pieces of change rolled past the vial, nearly knocking it off.

"What would you rather face?" asked Porter, lowering the pistol. "An early divorce, or 5 to 15?"

Just as Porter was about to punctuate his decision by puncturing me, mom's camera and my car keys skidded by and knocked the vial down. The magnet on my key chain promptly stuck to Porter's head, causing a glitch in his system. His right eye, which had been replaced by targeting sensors and a tiny video version of an eye, suddenly started showing rows of numbers. Porter's arm spazzed as he tried to gain control. I grabbed the vial and downed the Stuff in desperation. Porter dropped the gun, then pulled off the magnet with his normal hand. While I began to gag on the Stuff, Porter picked up the gun and checked the camera for the film.

"Where the Hell's the film?!'"" he demanded.

"Shit, I forgot to check it," I lamented, keeping my face turned away.

"Bullshit!"

Oh, yeah, I forgot. Although empty, I had been assured that there was film in the camera. (Way to go, mom.)

"Gimme the film!"

"Not much of a— Cough! —threat to a guy you're gonna shoot anyway."

Porter put a bullet into the chamber and aimed at my head.

"End of the line, punk," he growled in a really bad Dirty Harry imitation.

With that I turned around. Even with only half a vial, a bright green light was pouring out of my eyes and mouth.

"Oh, *very* original," I laughed, amused. "And I bet you still listen to Night Ranger too."

Porter's squeal nearly drowned out his gunshots as they echoed down the hill and valley of the ruined park. Did I mention what the Stuff is and where I got it? Hmmm, maybe I should start over.

CHAPTER 2 (Mark): End the Kissy Time

By the time Pine Hill's finest arrived, I had already retrieved my car, gun, overcoat and disc player. No Ska', just a bootleg CD with an STP concert and half of "In Utero". It was good calming music after a hard day of work.

Porter's cybernetics were playing havoc with his brain. He drooled as fax machine-type sounds emanated from his mouth. (Lucky for him I only brought half a vial.) Porter's human hand was tied to the tree, along with his torso. His cyber arm, ripped out at the shoulder, lay between his legs. I placed the cyber hand over his balls because, what fun is catching bad guys if you can't humiliate them, right?

"Hands in the air! Let's see the piece!"

The force of local cops was led by Lonny, an old buddy of mine from community college. A large vehicle — That looked like an *armored ambulance* — pulled up a little closer to Porter. The Philly cyber cops were here to take care of their own.

"What the fuck is this, Lonny?" I demanded, tossing my gun. "I call you in for `The Collar of the Week' and you shove a God damn bazooka in my face?!"

The Pine Hill locals relaxed, as Lt. Goda and his technicians got out of the ambu-tank. Goda was a balding, 40 plus cop. The first ever to be fitted with a cyber-prosthesis, but as he aged, his left leg, his real leg, shrank, while his cyber leg stayed the same. This made his walk a little ungainly as his twenty-year-old suit shambled its way toward me, spewing bad coffee breath and urgent questions.

"Whatda Hell happened? What did this to him?"

"Can I put my hands down?" I asked, perturbed. "I am a licensed Private Investigator."

"No. You think just because you have a P.I. license, you got the right to blow away drug dealers in a residential area?!"

"Hey, don't get testy with me because one of your *cyberboys* went nuts. I didn't put a gun to his head and make him sell drugs."

"Maybe you did."

"What?" I couldn't believe this guy and dropped my hands. "Lonny, are you gonna straighten this out? Or do I have to bust out your PBA card?"

"He's all right, lieutenant," Lonny meekly protested. "Fix is a friend. He's good people."

Goda's goons were already loading Porter into their vehicle and sticking him full of tubes and wires.

"Fix? What are ya?" sneered Goda. "Some kind of super? I don't like supers, kid. I especially don't like ones that go ripping out millions of dollars of police equipment."

"Well your `police equipment' was trying to blow my head off at the time!"

"Look, if you're trying to hide some rogue vigilante or Liberator..."

"Lonny," I pleaded. "I got a date with you-know-who, ten minutes ago. Can you wrap this for me?"

"Look, Lieutenant, I can vouch for him. He's not a super. Christ, he's practically an honorary Liberator."

"Fine, get out of here," Goda relented. "But I want a complete statement from him by 10 AM tomorrow morning!"

"Yeah-yeah-yeah," I scoffed. "You don't have any jurisdiction here. Go back to your side of the river, *Robodork*."

Goda looked as if he was about to lunge at me, but Lonny guided me out of danger. Goda simmered near the other side of his truck. Normally, I didn't goad the cops so much. (Especially the cops with ten million dollar thighs.) But I was all wound up from the Stuff.

"Man, Mark, what's with you?" asked Lonny.

"I'm sorry, Lon'. I get a little edgy after somebody tries to *kill* me." I got into the Nippon.

"Jesus, you still drive this thing?"

I looked at the little, black, Japanese coupe. Last week, someone had written "Wash Me" with their finger in the dirt on the hood above the dent and the big scratch. The dust from the parking lot had almost covered the letters. Guess I was due for a wash.

"Don't dis the Fixmobile. Do I dis your wife?"

"But you're not married to the car."

"You know what me and the Nippon have been through? We've traveled vast distances —through space and time —through Hell and back —once literally. Now *that's* loyalty. You don't get that from a wife, my friend. Just ask Johnny Carson."

Slowly, I began to roll the Nippon towards the exit, away from the shining police lights and gathering crowd.

"I'll see you tomorrow at ten," waved Lonny.

Just before I accelerated, I popped my head out of the window.

"I like to sleep in. Let's make it noon."

"Fix!"

As Lonny's cries echoed unanswered down the valley of the old water park, I popped in the soundtrack to "Pulp Fiction" and nudged the Nippon up Blackwood-Clementon road, onto 42, then 130 and ultimately, to the parking lot of my office near the Tally-Ho Arcade in Pennsauken.

Pennsauken, New Jersey, for those of you unfamiliar with the area, is a kind of half-way town. Half way typical suburb and half-way a ghetto. Half-way to Philadelphia and half-way to Cherry Hill. The only reason to stop there was because you were on the way to somewhere else. The town was right on the border of crime-ridden Camden (and, as they say, even the Mafia avoids Camden), which meant Pennsauken was the likely target for the criminals that were too lazy to drive the extra five minutes to the real suburbs. The town had this weird dichotomy of urban problems mixed with suburban responses. Every strip mall was withering due to the local economy, leaving every other store vacant and parking lots cracked and sprouting weeds.

But, hey, the rent on office space is righteous and its just far enough from Camden to give you odds you won't be robbed until you can find some place better. Don't ask me how the Tally-Ho stays open. Arcades do loser business even in the good neighborhoods and the Tally-Ho attracted the sort of loitering, skate-punk, nothing-better-to-do-with-their-life crowd that even had me shaking my fist and muttering, "Kids today, they ain't got no respect for nuthin', dag nabbit." More than one scratch on the hood of the Nippon was due to the skate punks attempting to leap it and land on the board as it rolled out on the other side.

As I pulled up, one of the skate punks was attempting to do that very maneuver to you-know-who's car. But the punk knew better when he saw me pull in the lot. He gathered speed, then made a sharp turn away from the fire engine red Neptune.

I thought about saying something as I got out of the car, but it was only a few years ago that I would've been the skate punk. Actually more like 15 years. Christ, has it been that long? Jeez, I gotta move out of my parents' place.

"Where have you been?" barked Mindy, the second I walked through the door. "I called your mother and everything. I thought you were just taking pictures."

I won't bore you with the full story of my relationship with Mindy. (Bul-*leeve* me, you don't have that kind of time.) Suffice it to say we've run hot and cold for over a decade. Like Sam and Diane, Hepburn and Tracy, Manson and Tate, Buttafuco and Fisher. We were on the low end of a "kissy-time", where our romance would burn like white-hot magnesium for a week, then flicker out as we started to get on each other's nerves again. To Mindy's credit, she was still asking me sensible questions. "Where have you been?" as opposed to "Why do you always do this to me?".

"Hon'," I grinned as best I could. "I'm a little stressed right now. Someone just tried to kill me."

"Oh, God. You better call your mother right now."

"Tch, why? What did you tell her?"

"I don't know. I told her... About... Your case..."

"Oh, Gaaaawwwwddd..."

"I didn't mean to! I forgot who I was talking to. I — Look, just call her."

Ah, the women in my life. Even Samson laughs at me.

"No, ma, I am not shot," I talked into the phone a few minutes later. "It wasn't like that. I walked in on a drug deal and called the cops. That's basically it."

"Mom, why would the ambulance people have to look at me if I wasn't hurt?"

"No, it's not like a concussion if you're almost shot. Look, I'm fine. It's just a job. It's over."

"Yes, I'm getting paid. Look, me and Mindy are late for something. I'll talk to you tomorrow, 'kay?"

"Bye-bye."

"Thank you!" I said to Mindy, hanging up the phone. "Why do you tell my mother *things*?!"

"She's your mother. She was worried."

"Yeah, but she's no good in a crisis. Remember the toll booth incident I told you about?"

Mindy exhaled, indicating that I told that story too many times. Then she smiled and, for the first time, I saw her today. Her pert nose. Her blonde, permed locks. Her wicked, little, 5' 7" bod wrapped in a smartly-done mini-dress. Her eyes flickered and danced with a light that could fill up a room, laugh in your face, demean you and love you all at the same time. I could feel the vibes between us and when we were in sync, it was just the best. God how I wish it would last.

Then I did something that you can only do with a decade of history between two people. I went into the bathroom and took a piss with the door open.

"God! I hate when you do that!" Mindy whined as the phone rang.

"Could you answer that? I have my hands full," I snickered.

Mindy moved into the next room to my secretary's unused desk. She answered the dusty phone, pushing aside the "Back in 10 minutes" sign to sit down.

"Inevitable Investigations, may I help you?" answered Mindy in her best secretary's voice. "Mark, it's Smitty!"

"Tell him we're leaving now."

"He says to take your time, he's not going to make it."

"Oh, you gotta be kiddin' me!"

I popped back into the lobby trying to find a presentable shirt to change into. Mindy had already hung up.

"What did he say?"

"He said that he couldn't make the opening, something came up. Did you actually expect Smitty to show up for something when he was expected?"

"No, but it is *his* nightclub that's opening. Sven's gonna be pissed. What shirt should I wear?"

I held up two "respectable" choices of club wear. Very fashionable, circa 1988.

"Is *that* all you have? You know, there are these things called malls, where you can get new clothes. I thought you went shopping with your mom."

"I got busy. Black or blue. I don't want to stand in line."

"Black," she sighed, resigned to my fashion-challenged sensibilities. "A polo shirt with a skull..."

"It's Professor Skullmore from the *Terroroids* cartoon," I informed her snobbishly. "You know, the guys at the arcade love this shirt."

I slipped the shirt on and we were out the door. Then the phone rang and I went back in. Should've left. It was Mrs. Porter.

"Inevitable Investigations, this is Fix.

"Yes, well, I'm sorry, Mrs. Porter, but—-

"Well, at least you know he's faithful.

"What do you mean, you knew he was selling drugs?! Why didn't you tell me?! I almost got killed!

"Getting the police involved was inevitable! You should've known that!

"You bet your ass you have to pay me. You don't— Hello? God dammit!"

I slammed the phone down, slammed the door and got into the Neptune. I stewed in silence for a while, leaving Mindy with the uncomfortable gap of silence for a change.

CHAPTER 3 (Narrator): The Last Disgrace

Takashi was Kai's hotheaded cousin. Of all the Arikas, he was unmatched in martial arts, despite his notorious temper. And with a sai or nagasu in his hand, he was just about the most lethal fourteen-year-old on the planet. Kai's older brother, Hwan, had ordered him not to pursue the matter. Revenge would only be a matter of time. The Yakuza would buy the police report, get the appropriate names and make the appropriate kill.

But Takashi's temper got the best of him. Leading a group of gangbangers, he went on a rampage, cutting homeless people as they lay in a half-daze on the sidewalk. Even some of the older, more seasoned posse members were sickened by his callousness. Eventually, they left him in a bar in Olde City. After pouring on a good buzz, Takashi felt mean enough to cut open just about anybody. He cornered a junkie near Elfreth's Alley a few hours later.

"Dirty bum!" he screamed, as he beat her with the hilt of his little sword. "Who you kill last night, huh? You know what I am saying!"

"Didn't...mean to..." gasped the emaciated woman. "Need... my shit..."

She reached for a tiny bag containing four syringes in a purple plastic baggie. Takashi stomped them to pieces.

"Now you lick it off the ground, huh?!" he tormented.

Takashi quickly grew bored of his human punching bag. She was so disoriented, Takashi began to wonder if she even knew he was here.

"What does it mean?" she mumbled. "Voice...in my head..."

Takashi propped her against a wall, took a few steps back and did his patented flip slice, cutting her while in mid-air. He landed four feet away and admired his handiwork. She was still standing.

"The cut is so clean," he admired. "She doesn't even realize yet."

The woman took a few last gasps, then stopped short. Suddenly, here whole torso opened like the maw of an animal. The interior of her body had been ravaged by some semi-transparent, living goo. Takashi's eyes widened in fear, as the goo wrapped around him. He screamed in terror as the goo pulled him closer to the bizarre junkie.

"If one of us lives..." she intoned. "We all live..."

CHAPTER 4 (Mindy): **Mindy at the Wheel**

Don't get me wrong. I love Mark, I really do. But it's times like this that make me want to open the passenger side door and shove him onto a dark highway at seventy mph. Look at him.

I mean, he's had all day to get ready for this and he's a mess. He combs his hair once a *day*. He waits until his clothes actually rip before replacing them. And when he finally does, he runs to shop twenty minutes before we have to go somewhere.

Why must he cut everything so close to the bone? It's always the last minute; always rush-rush to be on time or be reasonably late. I've tried to help him. Lord knows I've tried.

But Mark's stubborn. He still dresses like a college student. Still lives with his parents. Still heaves whatever life has to offer him in a pile, hoping to sort it out later.

His goatee is always crooked! I think he shaves it that way on purpose just to irk me. And that damn hat, I'd like to tie him to a chair and make him watch me pop it in a furnace.

Then again, he's the only one of my friends who hasn't turned into his parents. I mean, Mark's not big on nightclubs, but he never turns down the opportunity to go anywhere, any day, anytime. Everyone else that's past twenty-five is always, "I gotta get up for work", "Can't get a baby-sitter" or "What's the sense, I'm already married?" But not Mark, never Mark. It's always, "Let's go, baby!". And it's always fun. Even when we end up in some dive, staring at the walls — He always makes it fun.

But God, just once, I wish he'd act like an adult. Like a man.

"Hey, wanna get water ice?" he suddenly asks, seeing a sign.

I give him the look. The "What are you, fucking nuts?" look.

"C'mon, we're already late."

Reluctantly, I pull over, but before I can give him my order, he bounces out of the car to the counter. I want cherry, but he'll come back with strawberry. He never remembers.

"They were out of strawberry, so I got you raspberry. You want to taste the bubble gum flavor?"

I gag and pull back onto the highway.

"It's got real chunks of bubble gum," he tempts.

"No, thanks," I reply, laughing despite myself. "That is *so* disgusting."

"So, anything exciting happen in the world of text book publishing?"

"No." At first, I stifle the urge to say it, but then I can't help myself. "Mark, that woman on the phone..."

"Nothing to worry about, we had a verbal contract—"

"Tch, Mark..."

"What? It'll hold up in court. She'll pay me, don't worry."

"Are you going to make this month's office rent?"

"Mindy..."

"Mark, you're almost thirty. Do you know that most of the people you graduated with have houses and kids? You don't even have a checking account!"

"What am I supposed to do? Tie up a hundred dollars just so I don't have to pay a service fee? The banks are rip offs anyway."

"You know what I mean..."

"I know, you know, I know."

"You live with your *parents*, Mark!"

"Oh, don't start..."

"Well?! Don't you think its about time you moved out and got your own place? I lived with my folks until I was twenty-five and I felt like a *loser*. Not that you're a—-"

"You'd better say that."

"Haven't you at least thought about it?"

"Yes!" he admits, forcing himself to answer. "But if I have to pay for an apartment and the office, the office would have to go. Then I'd have no rent for the apartment."

"But you could——"

"I'm *not* going back to work for someone else. I like my parents, they don't mind me livin' there, what's the big deal?"

"Don't you ever think about our—" I stop myself. What's the use? He's Mark. He's Fix. And that's all he's ever gonna be. "Forget it."

"What?"

"Just... Forget it."

I give him the opening to press me for an answer, but this is the path Mark fears to tread. I watch his face as he wipes away the consequences, his id grabs the controls and the car is full of fun again.

"Hey, I think MMR is doing a Cars retrospective," he grins a knowing grin from ear to ear. "You remember the Cars, right Min'?"

When I was in college, Mark bought me a tape with the Cars greatest hits. It was the only music we both liked. I'd play it at top volume to hide the sounds of our love-making that permeated the thin walls of the dorm. Even now, I get a little tingle just hearing, "Let's Go".

We get to Delaware Avenue in Philly. It's a weird street. It's about eight car widths wide, no sidewalk and about a million potholes. But somehow, every trendy club in Philly has been built here on or near the water. Smitty's club is no different; completely inaccessible to sensible parking.

I offer to pay for valet parking, but Mark won't hear of it. He makes me drive around and find a space in some dirty, little alley four blocks away. Sure, what does he care? His car's back in Jersey.

"Okay, we'll hang in the club for a few hours, then head over to Sven's probably. Maybe stop at Ret's in between. That okay with you beautiful?"

"Yeah," I relented. "If we're not mugged on the way to the club."

"This is Philadelphia, hon'. World's capital of superheroes and discount spandex outlets," he assures, looking up. "Look! Up in the sky!"

There are just certain things that amaze me about Mark. I mean, sure, you might think that superheroes are crawling all over Philadelphia if you just watch the news on TV. But I worked in Philadelphia four years before I actually saw one. Mark just mentions them, looks up in the sky and sure enough, there's the cape.

"Which one is that?" I ask, squinting at the red dot in the sky.

"I don't know. Ever since the Liberators changed to those red uniforms, they all look alike. It's kinda spooky."

People flying overhead is normal, but red uniforms are spooky. This is the logic I have to deal with.

"Wait a minute! That's Mr. Quantum! I know him! Hey, Scott! Scott!"

Mark suddenly goes tearing across an abandoned lot, waving his arms in the air like a maniac. Mark's friend Jonny used to be a Liberator and he's always dragging Mark to the superhero parties and events. I'm not really impressed with celebrities (unless its Brad Pitt or Antonio Banderas), but Mark's got stars in his eyes. You think movie stars are odd, superheroes. Feh. They're just plain weird.

"Hello citizen!" bellows Mr. Quantum as he hovers above us.

Mr. Quantum was stuffed into a red uniform with white and blue trim. The Liberator logo was emblazoned over a clearly embossed name tag, as if anyone would actually forget his name. He had a bushy mustache and a bad haircut. He sort of looked like a muscular version of Jess from *When Harry met Sally*. Unfortunately, he dropped his helpful personae as soon as he got close enough to recognize Mark.

"What can I— Oh. It's *you*."

"Scott, come down and meet my main squeeze, Mindy."

"First off, I'm on patrol here, not a tour of the city," he fumed. "Third - *Second off,* you're lucky I don't zap your ass for what you did at the Christmas party!"

"All I did was kiss a girl under the mistletoe," explained Mark, to both me and Mr. Q. "I didn't know she was with you."

"You think I'm stupid or something?" insisted Mr. Q. "You think I don't know what's goin' on? I got powers and abilities far beyond those of mortal men! I *know* what's goin' on!"

"Scott—"

"When I'm in the suit," corrected Scott. "It's Mr. Quantum. Okay? And for your information, Gloria left with me, not with you, okay? You and your little chippie, here, just go about your business before I run you in for obstruction of justice."

Mark turned away from Mr. Q and grimaced at me. I guess he didn't realize how touchy some people can be. Mr. Quantum made a frustrated face, than soared off into the night sky with his bruised, little ego.

"God," said Mark as he guided me away. "What a dick. He was so nonchalant at the party."

"So," I said coyly. "Tell me about this girl you kissed."

He turns on his heel, takes my hand and suddenly kisses me. Mark knows how to kiss. Another plus.

"She   was   a   *dog*   compared   to   you,"   he   smiles   roguishly.

"Yeah, I'll bet," I say suspiciously. "I hope Smitty's club has something to do or at least has decent dance music."

"There is no such thing, my little Fly Girl. It's like good country music. It just don't exist in enough quantity to make a difference."

I look back at my car, probably for the last time.

"You brought your gun, right?"

"Sure. If I ever see Smitty again, I'm gonna shoot him."

CHAPTER 5 (Goda): A Day Late & an Arm Short

Betkin and Johnson — we called them "Beavis and Butthead" back at HQ — were trying to get Porter's cybernetics back on line. The rookie, Cunningham, was at the wheel and I was in the passenger seat wishin' I had taken the disability option.

"He gonna be all right, lieutenant?" asked Cunningham as gently as a thousand-dollar whore. "I mean, they can save him, right?"

"Who knows? His cybernetics are a lot more complicated than mine. Hell, sometimes I can't even get up to pee in the morning."

Cunningham turned a little pale.

"I'm jokin' kid. Look, take it easy. Ninety-five percent of the force never even has to get the option of replacement parts. And most guys don't even take 'em when they're offered. You keep your eyes open and your vest on and you'll be okay."

Butthead suddenly piped up. "Goda, I think he's awake."

I moved to the back to talk to Jason. The guy was in my squad for a year, I owed him the benefit of the doubt.

"Jase', it's Tommy Goda. Can you hear me?"

B & B had shut off his cybernetics completely. If any of his internal circuits were damaged, it would require major surgery. If the P.I.'s charges were even half true, he'd never get it.

"I— I can't feel my arm, Tommy."

"That's because it's in a box underneath ya. What the hell happened, Jase'?"

"I followed this guy. Fix. On a lead. He was dealin' drugs with my Jamaican connections."

I gave B & B the nod to move up front with Cunningham.

"I didn't hear that, Jason."

"It was a bust, man. A bust!"

"God dammit, Jase'!" I growled, trying not to lose it. "Don't make it any worse for yourself. One of the Jamaicans already fingered you."

"Oh, God."

Jason started to sob. Even the cybernetic side of his face shed a tear.

"Why didn't you come to me, Jase'? If it was about money..."

"I couldn't, Tommy. I was already on probation! God I'm so stupid!"

Jason sobbed into my arm and I looked away, wondering how I missed the cries of a drowning man.

"But Tommy, you gotta watch this Fix guy. I remember him from Uriah Case last December. There's something weird about him, I'm not kiddin'."

"There's something weird about everybody in Jersey. And in case you don't know it, we got superheroes patrollin' City Hall and you and me look like extras from the Terminator movies. Christ, Boss Viggio's got a fucking witch doctor for a bodyguard. And you wanna talk about weird. He just some punk kid with a gun permit."

"Tommy, I'm tellin' you. I've seen it. He ain't human."

CHAPTER 6 (Fix): Fixing Drinks

Smitty's nightclub was called "Alien Blue" and was decked out in retro science fiction props combined with MTV sensibility. A "Robby the Robot" stood motionless behind the bar in a pair of knee-length, day glow surfer shorts. Old movie posters for "Them", "Day of the Daleks" and "Robot Jox" hung in the darkness between flashing video monitors of music videos and "Plan 9 from Outer Space". It was Smitty's little joke, but only me and Sven knew enough to smile.

Of course, me and Mindy took twenty minutes to get inside, despite our "V.I.P." status. Sven sat in a private booth in the dim light of the "Martian Room" with two swimsuit models draped over him like a vest. Sven loved the club, of course, but he loved anyplace that served beer in the quantities that he drank.

Of course, Sven was seven feet tall, built like Schwarzenegger, talked like Captain Picard on steroids, sported designer sunglasses, three-hundred-dollar muscle shirts, a big blonde Mohawk and two braids in the back as thick as your arm. Did I mention Sven was from Asgard? Don't worry, I won't start over.

"Fix!" he boomed from across the nightclub. Even with the music, the walls shook. "Get thee a drink! The Son of Thor demands drinking companions!"

Mindy and I were about to join Sven and his busty companions, when Mindy pulled a "Mindy" on me.

"Okay, Mark. Are we together or alone?"

God, I hate this! Since we were getting along so well, I had already resigned myself that Mindy and I were in boyfriend-girlfriend mode. Now, here she was, at the last second, with sweet bosoms in front of me, giving me an out. Her sudden suggestion took me off guard. I wasn't ready for the test. I began to think that she planned to meet one of her "90210 boys" here and that I would be left taking the train home. But, if Sven was already with both these women (and I've seen him go home with as many as six) then I'd be left with my dick in my hand.

All this flashed through my mind as we traversed the distance and the ten seconds in time it took to get me and Mindy to Sven's table. Mindy or new boobs? Mindy's boobs were nice, but new boobs were always nicer. And new.

"Mark?"

But if I say we're together, I'll look like I'm clinging to her. That puts me right into a bad slide with Mindy, always. Then I end up getting my calls screened, waiting for her at restaurants, caving in and seeing chick movies.

"Mar-ark..." she mutters as we get closer.

And I'll look like a total dork if she starts cruising the dance floor solo. Some skeezeball with a ponytail will offer her a line and she'll leave me hangin' just like that time in Delaware. But, then again, we were getting along just famously up to now. And she did drive. Christ this is a nightmare.

"Uh, alone," I mutter under my breath.

"What?!"

"Together, together," I correct myself loudly enough for all to hear. I put my arm around my fuming babe. "Here I am, together with Mindy."

"Very well," Sven replies a bit perplexed. "Fix, this is Casandra, my escort and Sabrina, a friend of Smitty's."

Great. Worst case scenario. Mindy's fuming at me and Sven's sitting here with an extra pair of Class-A, major yaboos. My life sucks.

"Hi," Mindy says icily. "How's the salon, Jonny. Jonny? Or is it, Sven?"

"Whatever suits you, my dear. Tho' I will always be Sven, Son of Thor, to my customers and to television viewers on the Greater Eastern Seaboard, I am Jonny Plazzz! President, Proprietor and Chief Hair Stylist of the Jonny Plazzz Hair Care Corporation! Now where is Smitty?"

"Bad news, big guy..." I begin.

"Ye gods!" Sven bellows knowingly, pounding the table in disbelief. "That man will be missing from his own funeral!"

Sven apologized to Sabrina, while I tried to play catch up with Mindy. If I'm lucky, I can throw her mood switch back to "happy" before she pisses all over the evening.

"Hon, can I get you a drink? You hungry?"

"Oh, I don't know. Get me something with ice. I'm feeling rather *frigid* this evening."

Hey, it's working.

"I'll be right back."

"Wait, Fix. The Son of Thor shall join you."

Sven and I ordered from the bartender. He was dressed as a Starfleet captain and looked just thrilled to be serving us.

"What can the *replicator* get you gentlemen?" he says rolling his eyes, not even bothering to conceal his boredom.

"Banana daiquiri, one virgin, one not."

"A tankard of ale and two more of— What is it? Wine coolers? So, Fix," begins Sven, nearly slapping my shoulder into dislocation. "Let's see what trouble we can brew this night!"

"I'm already in enough trouble, but thanks," I politely decline. "Did the Orlando salon open?"

"Barely. The bribes cost me tenfold. It's as if the whole province of Florida is owned by that man's blasted mouse!"

"I never liked that mouse, if it's any consolation. But the duck's cool."

"How doth thee fair with Inevitable Investigations?"

"I doth think I'll be in court again. I gotta start taking fees up front."

"The New Brunswick salon could use another security evaluation..."

"Thanks, Sven, but I'm not a charity case just yet. No, wait a minute, I am. How about Tuesday?"

Sven snatched a Martian tankard before the bartender could set it in front of him. He lifted it skyward, partially splashing the jaded server.

"To Tuesday! And victory!"

"Just how many of those has he had?" I said out of the side of my mouth to the bartender, as Sven consumed yea verily.

"I dunno, I lost track after the twenties. Who's gettin' this?"

I grabbed the drinks.

"Put it on Smitty's tab and tell him to call me."

Sven and I went back to the table, but Mindy was gone. I was tempted to just sit down and continue the evening with Sabrina, but I was determined to set things right with Mindy. Grabbing the daiquiris, I made a quick circle of the club, forgetting which one was the virgin. I spotted Mindy in the restroom vestibule and then my nightmare got worse.

"Sweetie, darling, how *are* you?"

It was Mindy's friend Viv and her dealer/boy-toy, Victor. Viv was Mindy's binge-buddy. They'd take week-long trips together, get ripped in some tropical paradise, then come back with hangovers and suitcases void of panties. Viv looked like some dried-up prom queen, with an impossibly thin figure, glazed eyes with color contacts and a designer pharmacy in her purse. She gave me an amused sneer as I approached and treated me as if she was personally responsible for crushing male libidos everywhere. I hate Viv. She was like the worst side of Mindy embodied in human form. Well, almost human.

"Mark, Sweetie, Mindy tells me you're about to close shop again. Oh, *do* try and save that *lovely* imitation leather sofa in your waiting room."

Viv was only making fun of my furniture. I guess she was in a good mood. Victor's laugh followed Viv's, even though he hadn't been paying attention to the joke. I couldn't hate Victor, only because he was so fucking pathetic. One of those pretty boys whose looks were finally leaving him. He didn't know it, wouldn't acknowledge it, but couldn't understand why people were treating him differently. I felt sorry for him. You had to be smart to stay out of prison and deal drugs these days. Victor was destined to be ass candy for some very horny felons. He wore a leather bomber jacket, expensive slacks and worn Dockers. He had sort of a "Jeff Spacoli" hairdo, but the blonde dye job had worn out its welcome weeks ago, not that his drug-addled cranium and bleary eyes would notice. I said hi to Viv, but gave him the nod.

"W'sup, man," he half mumbled, half laughed.

I got right to the point.

"You coming back to the table?"

"C'mon, Sweetie," Mindy replied in her best "Ab Fab" voice. "Have some fun with us."

"It's a rave, darling, a rave," added Viv, tempting me with some chemical substance, then downing it herself. She offered some to Mindy, who surprisingly refused.

"No, thanks, darling. Victor, did you bring the coke?"

I tried not to say anything. I really don't believe in telling people how they should live their lives. Mindy's always been a party girl, but you'd think she'd outgrown it by now. Frustration got the best of me. I downed one of the daiquiris, smashed both glasses in the trashcan, grunted and stormed away. Viv mocked my grunt as I left.

"Oh, c'mon, Mark," pleaded Mindy. "I've been good. It's just tonight."

"Tch, let him stew, Sweetie..."

As Viv's voice was drowned out by the music, I marched into the restroom. I think I just needed to be away from all women for a moment. To take seek refuge from the sounds of gaggling hens and cocaine demons that had momentarily consumed Mindy. Then something truly magical happened. Victor followed me in.

He sniffed and coughed his way across the room, sounding like he had caught the flu from Ska-boy #2. Victor was scouring the floor of the bathroom for a razorblade he had dropped earlier. What an idiot. He was halfway across the bathroom before he realized I was leering at him in the mirror. Then he suddenly bolted for the door, but I intervened and threw him up against the handblowers.

"Fix, man, what?" he said rather incoherently.

"Hi, Victor. What did I tell you about selling to Mindy?"

"You said not to sell to her and not to let her know you're threatening me."

Gee, maybe he isn't that stupid.

"Then what the *fuck* were you doing out there?!"

"What was I supposed to do? Not sell to her? Then she'd know, right? C'mon, man."

"I'm sorry, Victor," I apologized, again feeling genuinely sorry for him. "I will have to penalize you."

Carefully searching through his pockets of syringes and drug paraphernalia, I came up with Victor's baggie of coke. I felt like flushing the whole thing, but I didn't want to get the little guy killed. He foolishly put himself in hock to his supplier, a vicious Oriental gentlemen known for breaking blocks of wood with his head and breaking blockheads like Victor with pieces of wood.

"Hey, c'mon, man," he whined, his voice soaring higher. "I swear, man, I swear!"

I don't even think he knew what he was swearing to, but it didn't matter. I suddenly started to shake violently, spilling coke everywhere. As I shook, Victor did too, the contents of his pockets dancing their way out. His hashish pipe skittered under a toilet, while one of the syringes went into my hand. Then, suddenly, I was seeing everything in double. Victor's eyes popped opened to their maximum breadth and he looked at me with genuine surprise.

"Whoa, I knew that ecstasy was bad, but..."

I turned and looked at the mirror. While I was shaking, I had suddenly grown a second head. The damn Stuff was giving me a belated side effect. In shock, I spilled Victor's baggie, dropped it on the floor and then moved toward the counter. Fortunately, the bathroom was void of other patrons, but I had to pull it together before anyone else saw the freak show. Victor scrambled for the baggie, sniffed the biggest pile from the floor, then tripped his way out of the mens' room.

Pulling the syringe out of my hand and splashing cold water into my face - faces — I tried to determine if I really had two heads or was just hallucinating that I had two heads. Once, I thought the Stuff had turned the tips of my fingers into snakeheads, but it turned out I was just hallucinating. I splashed one face, than the other.

"My you're a handsome devil," I said to the other head

As if this grotesque mutation wasn't enough to spoil my evening, my extra head answered me back in a deadly serious tone.

"Mark, you better get your shit in gear. Smitty's going to need your help."

"Whoa— I didn't think that."

"You better find him quick or he may never show his face again."

Unnerved by this *unnerving* chain of events (did I mention it was unnerving?), I bent down to splash the second face, just to make sure I could feel it. I stood up, the water went over my shoulder and down my back. I was amongst the human race again. Sven popped in.

"Ye gods, Fix. Are you going to piss all night?! There's wine, women and song, lad! C'mon!"

Exiting the bathroom, I was suddenly immersed in the pounding sounds of my favorite Trent song, "Wish" off his Broken EP. A crowd began to mosh and I charged in. I caught glimpses of Sven, the models, Mindy and Viv. The mosh got whipped into a frenzy as it surged and I let it take me. There's not a problem in existence you can't forget about after being in the mosh pit. Hell, you're too worried about your immediate personal safety for anything else to matter. The sweat, the pounding, the utter chaos. I was lost in a cacophony of arms, torsos, flashing lights and Reznor screams. The crowd was lit on everything from wine spritzers to acid-laced lollipops, but I was stone cold sober.

And I was gone, baby

CHAPTER 7 (Viv): To the Victor goes the Spoiled

What a ghastly little club! Who on *Earth* would design a nightclub with such fatal interior design, darling? Not me. God, I was bored with it before I made the first pass. Stamp the expiration date yesterday; you're all done, darling.

Blue something. The club, I mean. Of course, I was doing my usual charity work, trying to mate Mindy with something *higher* on the evolutionary scale than her terminal boy*fiend*, Mark. Turns her into an utter *bore* at times. Tonight was no exception. After a few *sensational* lines, we were tweaked for a night of dancing at someplace tasteful. I pulled Mindy out a fire exit, sending off bells and whistles, which couldn't be heard inside over the music. Outside was this disgusting little alley, where Victor was making some extra cash by selling off the remainder of his baggie. He's a dear, but I'll soon have to lose him. Damaged goods and all.

"Victor! Victor, help me!"

Mindy held onto the sides of the fire exit. Poor girl actually wanted to stay.

"I can't, Viv, I can't," she giggled coyly. "Why don't you just stay?"

"Not another minute, I won't!"

I let go of Mindy and she nearly toppled backwards. I looked for Victor, but he was gone. God! He's so useless sometimes.

"Victor! Help me! Honestly, darling, you have to start seeing other people. Why must you always go back to that bedpost of a sleeping companion?"

"Are you saying he's hung like a bedpost? I've got to start paying more attention in bed."

"Oh, please, darling. He could be hung like an eight-foot grizzly and he'd still be about as interesting as moss! You could do better. You know you can. Come along, I know where we kind find a whole barful of steroid-abusing muscle men! There's your bedpost, darling!"

"I can't. I'm staying."

"Tch, I thought you wanted to make him miserable."

"I do, that's why I'm staying."

"All right, then. One toot for the road?"

I drew my gold-plated coke carrier, with the matching straws, but we had already sniffed it in the bathroom. I went for the backup supply under the make up case, but no such luck. Dammit all! Why can't I live in a country with sensible drug laws?!

"Victor! Get your carcass over here, darling! Victor?"

Finally, the creepy little bastard walked into the light. He just about gave me the fright of my life, which isn't the healthiest of things to have with a heart racing on coke.

"Dammit, Victor, stop playing around and hand over the stash."

"I'm sorry, I sold it all."

Well, that was it! I don't know why I put up with Victor for so long. Now suddenly, he was out of coke and, from the sound of it, had somehow sobered up. God, as if he wasn't unbearable enough.

"Good-bye, Viv," added Mindy, pecking me on the cheek.

"See you for Sunday brunch? You can't miss the champagne breakfast this week."

"Of course, Darling. Tah."

Mindy smiled, waved and danced her cute little ass back into the club. I'm not a lesbian, darling, but if I were, it would *have* to be with Mindy. On a night like this, I could almost consider switching. I lied about the muscle men. Parade Mindy around and take the scraps left behind is my usual strategy. It was getting to be too much work picking someone up at a club.

"Want to call it a night?" cooed Victor, snaking his arms around me.

"Victor," I giggled, taken aback by this sudden burst of boldness. "You haven't held me like this since we got lit on the ferry."

Well, what can I say? Either Mindy and I had just about the worst lines of coke or something was very different about Victor. It was like someone had completely transformed his body language. His body seemed so sure of itself. Lean, mean again. Hard. Can't let that go to waste, can we?

If we had stayed any longer in the cab back to my apartment, that taxi driver would've had a show. Victor was pawing me like a zoo polar bear with an ice block during the summer. He even smelled differently. Musky. Damp. Humid. I can't describe it, but I liked it.

If I was with anyone else but Victor, I would've simply died! My apartment was dreadful! I was in mid-redecoration, half late Colonial mixed with neo-Modern. It was like Ben Franklin's flat with Andy Warhol's furniture.

"I like your place," said Victor, flashing a smile.

"Tch, you've been here before, darling. Haven't you? I'm sure you have."

"I worry about you...Viv."

What a dear! Victor was just all full of sweetness tonight.

"All those drugs can be very unhealthy."

"All in moderation, darling. I'm as healthy as a horse. Care for a bubble bath?"

"I'd like that. Can I use your stereo?"

"Certainly."

I put my tongue in his ear, then slinked away, leaving a trail of clothing as I walked to the Jacuzzi. Victor slid his jacket off, letting the moonlight glide across his wonderfully tan, washboard stomach. And all this time, I thought he was falling apart! Maybe it was just the light, but I hadn't been this hot since I accidentally set fire to my wig learning to free base.

Then the stereo came on. I was expecting Johnny Mathis or jazz or some kind of sex music. But suddenly I was hearing the most inappropriate song from the Beatles, of all people.

"Oh, God," I wretched, testing the water in the Jacuzzi. "Where on Earth did you find that in my CD collection?"

"Don't you like it?"

Like it? The song was "Run for your Life", not "Sex in the Jacuzzi".

"No. It's a bit poppy for what we're about to do, isn't it?"

"I like it. Viv, you don't have any allergies I should know about? Do you?"

"Oh, for God's sake, Victor. I've got condoms. Are you my doctor now? You want my whole blood work done?"

"As a matter of fact...I do!"

Suddenly, Victor's eyes turned all silvery, like mercury. He raised his hand, which seemed distorted, grossly large and pointed with knife-like fingernails. He moved so fast, I suddenly found myself on the floor, stunned. He stood above me, holding what looked like a piece of meat. Then he changed. His face and body turned into a completely different man, like out of a movie or something.

I could feel the carpet beneath me getting all wet and that's when I realized the bastard had flayed me wide open. Then Victor— Whoever the hell he was, just left me lying there, with that damn Beatles song continuing to play.

It was weird. I let out this sort of half laugh in disbelief. I was fading away, yet I wasn't crawling to the telephone to call the police. I wasn't screaming for a neighbor or a passerby to help me. All I could do was stare up at the ceiling. And, as the very life flowed out of me, only one thought came into my head. Not a past love, or my times with Mindy. Not a memorable high point or regret in my life, or even the fact I was dying in a partially redecorated apartment. All I could think of was...

"God, the ceiling looks *dreadful*..."

<u>CHAPTER 8</u> (Fix): Mindy Morning

"Ehhhhhhh..."

I am awakened by the hangover moans of Mindy. For some reason, we decided to crash on the uncomfortable floor in my room rather than the almost comfortable mattress I keep on it. Mindy is draped across me, her head resting on my right butt cheek, which I somehow twisted into position for her during the night. My clothes felt lose and Mindy's bra is draped on a nearby lamp. (No doubt we made an abortive attempt at sex.) A streak of very old poster putty is visible on the paneling on the opposite side of the room, where an ancient poster for the band "Neon Loser" lies curled up from the humidity on the floor. (It's a band I used to manage back in the day—and even their posters sucked.)

I can feel my muscles starting to kink and the back of my head is sore from leaning against the heating vent. I didn't drink a damn thing last night, but I suspect the Stuff contributed to my cottonmouth and a feeling of being spent. Why did we sleep on the floor? Oh, yeah. My mattress was covered with boxes of three-quarter-inch video tapes of porno outtakes. Last case. Long story.

"Ehhhhh"

I squint at the clock, but I can't see it without my glasses. When I put them on, I still can't see it because the lamp's in the way. As I jockey for a position, trying not to wake the Beast, she begins to stir. I freeze, hoping to somehow transfer her head to the edge of the mattress. Then mom walks in on us.

"Mark," she says, as if I'm still 8 years-old. "Have you seen my camera?"

I gesture frantically at Mindy's sleeping head, but its no use. Mindy's been around her too long. She's family. She has to suffer like everyone else. God, I gotta get my own place.

"It's 1:30," she informs me, gesturing at the piles of filthy clothes and papers. "Ya know."

"I know, ma. I know," I whine. "Do I have to clean it up right this minute? I got Mindy, here."

"Ehhhhhhh...."

"Tch. Is she all right?"

"Her stomach's a little upset. We were out kinda late."

She spots the bra dangling nearby, then looks at me disapprovingly. She thinks I broke the "No-sex-in-the-house" rule. Wait a minute, did she say it was 1:30?

"Did you buy your cousin a gift yet? The wedding's in three days."

"I know, ma, but——"

"And your suit's a rag. You said Mindy was going to take you shopping."

"I *know*, ma——"

"And your father wants the lawn fertilized before next weekend. You'd better do it before he does, you know how he gets. Did you actually wear that shirt last night?"

"I will. Yes. What time did you say it was?"

"1:30, how many times do I have to tell you? What are all these video tapes for?"

1:30?! I'm way late for Lonny.

"Oh, shit."

Getting up abruptly, Mindy klunks her head on the floor.

"Owww! Ehhh... Oh, hi, Mrs. M."

"Nice of you to stay over," Mom says icily, taking down the bra and tossing it to Mindy. "You know you're always welcome here, Mindy."

And with that, my mother walks away. Probably off to torture other victims. Mindy snatches up the bra and punches me.

"Ow!"

"You're supposed to lock the door!" she hisses, glaring at me through half-closed eyes.

"We didn't even *do* anything! You okay?"

Mindy doesn't say anything. She clamps her lips shut and makes the warning sound. She's gonna blow.

"No-no-no-no-no!" I intone, trying to get her into my bathroom.

Mindy doesn't make it. She starts hurling steady streams into my wastepaper basket.

"Huuuuuuuuuurrrkkkkk!"

The phone rings. I answer just so I don't have to hear her retch.

"Huuuuuuuuuurrrkkkkk!"

"Oh, God— Hello, Inevitable Invest— I mean, hello."

"Fix, my Sarge is just about to feed my ass to me!"

"I'm sorry, Lon'. Late night."

"Huuuuuuuuuurrrkkkkk!"

"Christ, what is that?"

"My, uh, toilet's backing up——"

"Huuuuuuuuuurrrkkkkk!"

Mindy's vomit reaches the edge of the basket.

"Oh, God! I'll see you in twenty, Lonny."

I hang up, dump out the poker chips and change from my giant "Mug o' Fun" and get it under Mindy's chin just in time.

"Huuuuuuuuuurrrkkkkk!"

"What were you *eating* last night?"

Mindy spits out the last remaining chunks in a vain attempt to cleanse her palate.

"Ugh. I don't remember," she mumbles. "You have any toothpaste?"

I don't know about you, but about the only thing that will make me vomit is the smell of somebody else's vomit. The whole house begins filling up with a smell that's making me downright nauseous. I dump the "Mug o' Spew" in the toilet, avert my nose, close my eyes and flush. Mindy walks in the doorway in a haze.

"Is my car okay?"

"Yes, it's outside."

I pick up the wastepaper basket full of barf. A little runs down onto my hand and I stifle the urge to drop it. The spew and the paper go into the toilet, but it takes a few flushes.

"This," I say to Mindy, gritting my teeth while trying not to inhale the fumes. "Is *really* disgusting!"

"Mark?" mom calls from the kitchen. "What's going on?"

"Nothing!"

Mindy smiles. She's not awake enough to help me, but is awake enough to enjoy my misery.

"Give us a kiss," she grins.

"Get-away-from-me! You got chunks on your chin."

"Ew," she replies, wiping her face.

I stew a bit, although I can't remember why I'm mad at her.

"You still mad about last night?"

Oh, yeah. Viv. The coke. I steal a glance down the hall to make sure mom's not in earshot for this.

"Mindy, you do what you want to do."

"Tch. Don't lay that on me! Don't do that!" she hisses back.

Here we go, right back into a dogfight. And all at a volume that a librarian couldn't hear.

"What do you want me to say? You promise me you won't do it and then you do. An afternoon joint is one thing—"

"Oh, yeah. Like I'm on my way to becoming a crack whore!"

Mayday, mayday. He's breaking up, he's breaking up.

"Why stop at coke, Min'? Why not sniff some paint? How 'bout some air conditioner fumes? Want some of that?!"

"Yeah, maybe I do! Like you don't do *anything*!"

She starts to storm away, but wait! He's pulling out of the dive!

"Min', the only reason I get mad is because I care about you. I know Viv's your friend, but look at her. She looks like your great aunt! That stuff adds *years* to you. Stick to pot. It makes you much happier."

"This is all about Viv, isn't it? You never liked her."

Bam! Smack into a mountain!

"I'll see you tonight. Here's the toothpaste."

I hand her the tube, kiss her on the forehead and exit. She leans into the bathroom mirror and starts looking for crow's feet.

"Hmm, don't bet on it."

Enroute to Lonny's station house, I scan the floor of the Nippon for appropriate background music. I wore out my John Cougar tape playing, "I need a lover that won't drive me crazy", so I settle for old PE and "Sophisticated Bitch". Hey, it's my car, I'll play what I want.

"I've made a statement, I said I'd testify— What more do you want, Lonny?"

I was sitting in a suburban squad room. Not at all like the movies. No endless parades of prostitutes. No psychotic biker types struggling to cause havoc. No constant ringing of phones. I was sitting in a quiet, sterile, air-conditioned cubicle with brand new furniture, while Lonny was trying to get me to say something nice about Jason Porter. The biggest distraction in the room was the dispatch operator's portable TV. It didn't have much atmosphere, but the donuts were fresh.

"I dunno. Did he really try to kill you *that* bad?"

"Yes! Look, don't go feeling sorry for Jason Porter just because he's a cop. The only person to blame is Jason Porter. C'mon, Lonny, it's almost five. Why am I still sitting here?"

Lonny looked down a little embarrassed and tapped his pencil.

"I got nuthin' else to do."

"Well, I'm not entertaining ya. Good-bye."

I got up and headed for the exit.

"Aw, c'mon," Lonny pleaded. He must've really been bored. "You wanna look at some more mugshots?"

"No!"

Lonny followed me out. He seemed real anxious to keep me there.

"Um, you goin' to the paintball rally this year?"

"Maybe," I said, casting suspicious glances everywhere. "I thought your wife wouldn't let you go anymore."

"Oh, uh, yeah— Well..."

We stopped at the front door. Outside, I watched Lt. Goda pull up in an unmarked van with two goonish sidekicks. I glared back at Lonny. "You bastard. You stalled me until they could get here."

"I h-had to. My captain ordered me."

"Just for that, I'm tellin' your wife about your bachelor party."

"Aw, c'mon!"

"Mr. Fix, we need to talk..." began Goda.

I made a vain attempt to get inside the Nippon. My mouth answered Goda, but my body continued on to the car.

"I'm sorry, Fix is inside. I'm his identical twin, Larry."

One of the goons answered my flip comment by nearly closing the driver's side door on my hand. Even so, the door never quite shut right.

"You have to lift up a little," I explained to the goon. "Here let me show ya."

The goons lifted me up by the arms and carried me to the van.

"Kidnapping in the parking lot of a police station. This completes the total break-down of society, everybody!"

"Get him inside," growled Goda.

It's a good thing the van was air-conditioned. I was sweating up a storm in my overcoat, which only added to the stink from last night. (I didn't have time to change.)

It's times like this when I could use a lap top computer to keep track of all my paranoid delusions. My first reaction was that they didn't believe the story I made up about Porter losing his arm in the fall. If that was true, they either were convinced I was a super or was in league with one. If the latter was the case, they would probably suspect Sven and leave it be. (Retired superheroes don't like to get bothered and the police don't like to bother them.) If they thought I was the super, for all I know, they could be taking me to some government laboratory for unspeakable scientific experiments.

Oddly enough, those two scenarios didn't bother me. What bothered me was that these were cops from Philadelphia and in my wilder youth, certain ones would routinely beat the living crap out of you if you were dressed like a punk and hung out on South Street. It didn't happen to me personally, but it did happen to just about everybody I knew who lived in and around South Street. (Not that a few of them didn't deserve it.) Here I was, the only living witness ready to send one of their buddies away. They didn't even have to plant a gun on me.

Well, despite my paranoid fantasies, I decided to go on the offense.

"Look, I got nuthin' to say to you guys. You want a statement? Have Lonny photocopy you one."

"This nothing to do with Porter," explained Goda. "Can you account for your whereabouts last night between midnight and three AM?"

Typical police interrogation tactics. Goda did all the talking, while the goons just stared at me.

"Yeah, I was in a nightclub with about four-hundred people. You want their phone numbers?"

Goda didn't like my smart-ass comments. He gave the goons a look and they both grabbed me.

"Hey-hey-hey-hey!" I protested.

The two goons didn't hit me, they just forcibly adjusted my seating arrangement. One goon held my by the lapels, while the other finally figured out he better remove my gun. Goda leaned toward me menacingly.

"Fix, you are a suspect in a murder investigation, so you'd better just give me a little cooperation."

"Fine. Tell me who died so I can make my denials and get the hell out of here."

"Do you know a Ms. Ruthann V. Nickelbaum?"

"No, can I go?"

"Are you sure you don't know her?"

"I don't know. In the realm of human experience, we may have met once. Her name doesn't ring a bell," I said impatiently. "Got a picture?"

"Yeah, here's her picture."

Goda handed me a crime scene photo. My heart sank and my bravado disappeared. It was Viv. She'd been flayed open like a carp.

"Oh, God. Viv...." I grimaced.

"Oh, so you do know her?" Now it was Goda's turn to be flip. "Found you in a group picture in her apartment. You two, uh, not get along?"

"To be honest, no, but I don't like the mailman either, that doesn't mean I'll cut him to pieces next time he brings the electric bill."

"How do you know her?"

"She's my girlfriend's best friend. Together they, uh, do chemical experiments, if you know what I mean."

"When did you last see her?"

"In a nightclub. Alien Blue. She left with her friend, Victor. Did you find him dead too?"

"No, why?"

"Victor's her shadow, they go everywhere together. He should've been the last person to see her alive."

"Unless he killed her."

"Victor can't count to *three*. He doesn't have the brains, the reason or the balls to kill anyone. But, the real target could've been Victor."

"How so?"

"Let me take a look at the crime scene—"

"You're nuts! You're still a suspect."

"I can help, I know some of their friends."

Goda handed me a pen and a piece of paper.

"Then make me a list."

"They're not gonna talk to you. Half of 'em got bench warrants."

"Look," insisted Goda. "You answer our questions, you give us the names and then you stay out of our investigation. Got it?"

Goda was grinding his teeth. My paranoid delusions suddenly didn't seem so paranoid.

"Oooookay," I agreed.

I gave them a list of names, but I left out a certain Oriental gentlemen with a propensity for wood. He had guys that worked for him that could kill you and never leave a mark, which made two good reasons why I wouldn't rat on him. After a few more questions and implied threats, Goda left me out of the van about a mile from the police station. He made it quite clear that if I meddled in his case that I would be endangering my P.I. license and the cartilage in my nose.

This was one of those rare times I used my cellphone. I didn't want the Goons & Goda trio dumping this on everyone. I called my high school buddy, Phil, who knew Viv and everyone else I knew. I called a few other mutual acquaintances and I even called Sven, just to let him know that I couldn't do the security check for a few days.

I just couldn't dial Mindy. It was the worst kind of news and I selfishly didn't want her to associate me with it. I decided to deliver the news in person, but in the back of my mind, I knew my personal grapevine would probably reach her before I got there.

Mindy was at her folks' place. Not far from the amusement park actually. She's had her own place for years, but still went over for the odd dinner now and again. Mr. Ballente greeted me at the door, I could hear Mindy crying inside.

"Hey, Mr. B," I said grimly. "I-I guess you all heard."

"Yes, it's a shame," he said back with the required sadness in his voice.

I took a step, but Mr. Ballente gestured that I shouldn't go inside.

"Mark, maybe you should go. Let Mindy come to grips with this."

I couldn't even look him in the eye. My shame was as palpable as my B.O.

"Yeah, I'll, uh— Tell Mindy I'll call her later."

"Yes. Good-bye, Mark."

"Bye."

Mr. Ballente shut the door and I walked away. I could feel the lump in my throat and the tears welling. I was all choked up, but not for Viv. All I could think to myself was, "God, you're a coward. You fucking coward!"

<u>CHAPTER 9</u> (Sven): Asgard's Favorite Son

T'was a day when I pined for the fiercest battlegrounds of Asgard! These mortals had such subtle forms of pain and torture. Tax forms, morning traffic, talk radio and, now, these damned building inspectors!

"Mr. Plazzz," he whined. "These fire extinguishers are two months past their expiration date. Now that's a clear violation of fire codes. What if you had a fire?"

"Then I would summon a great storm to quench the flame!"

This mortal fire inspector did scoff at the Son of Thor. For he did not believe in my wizardly prowess, granted unto me from Odin himself! Alas, he knew me not as the great hero of Asgard and the City of Brothers, but as the flamboyant Jonny Plazzz, Master of the Styling Gel. 'Lo! Manager Theo of my New Brunswick salon did approach.

"Hey, yo, boss. What's the hold up?" he inquired. "I got a 9:30 ten minutes ago."

"Patience Theo," I warned. "These New Brunswick inspectors are not so easily bribed."

"I heard that!" squawked the fire inspector from the next room.

Curse my luck! I traveled all the way from the City of Brothers to put the finishing touches on this, my fifth salon of New Brunswick. This mortal fire inspector cried out at every floorboard and window. Signs for a fire exit, directions for a fire escape— I wouldn't need this much information if I planned to burn the damned place down!

"Okay, that's it!" insisted the mortal fire inspector. "The ventilation on the second floor is *completely* unacceptable and the decor in this entire *building* is a fire hazard."

To punctuate his words, the mortal fire inspector brought his hand down on a magnificent statue I commissioned honoring the goddess Freya. But, at the time, I could not afford to have it carved from the finest of stone, so it was made from something the artist called "Styrofoam". It captured the mighty Freya with her sword aloft and her comely visage did greet the salon's customers with a warrior's stance. In his anger, the mortal fire inspector snapped great Freya's sword.

Such desecration does not go unpunished in Asgard, but this was New Jersey. Nevertheless, this mortal continued his whining musings until I could stand it no longer! I put my hand upon the hilt of my sword and prepared to wage war for the honor of my salon. But like a portent from the gods, Fix arrived and, seeing my distress, despite his own, intervened upon my behalf.

"Can we put the sword away until I talk to him *Beowulf*?" Fix advised. "It's behavior like that that got you kicked out of Asgard in the first place."

Fix was no warrior, to be sure, but his wit and guile would test Loki himself!

"Look, friend," he said to the inspector. "I know what you're goin' through. I used to work for Safe-Corp Inspection Services—"

"Well then you should've checked this place for your friend. This code violations are blatant and— Wait a minute. Didn't Safe-Corp get reamed in that 60 Minutes piece?"

"Sure, I was the guy that snitched on them."

"Wow! Really, we— Hey! Now I recognize you! You're Informant #2!"

"The one and only."

"I use a copy of that video in my training seminars! You probably saved a lot of lives. That company was run by the scum of the Earth."

"Yeah and one of my paychecks bounced."

"I guess you really know what you're doing— I suppose, I could give your friend an extra day. But only if you fix this place personally."

"Not a problem. Fix is my middle name."

And just like that, Fix had won the day! But the victory gave him no happiness and my proposal for drunken revelry was met with a sad countenance, which could mean only one thing. Fix and Lady Mindy were no more...again.

"Sven, I'm a complete fuck-up," he lamented in my office later. "She hates me. For real this time. I called her place for forty-eight hours straight. Christ! I'm supposed to the go to the funeral tomorrow."

"I would attend with you, but I fear my appearance would bring unwanted publicity to the ceremony. Perhaps I could speak to Mindy on your behalf."

"That's nice of you to offer, buddy, but— Well, you know Mindy. She has a thing about— You know, supers."

"Go to her then. Profess your love for her."

"I can't, don't you understand?! I dropped the ball. Screwed the pooch. Fucked the whole thing up!"

Being from Asgard, Fix's colloquialisms were lost upon me, but the urgency of his voice made the message quite clear.

"I'm a coward, Sven. I've completely lost her respect and I don't know how to get it back. What would you do? I mean, what's the manly Viking thing to do?"

"Slay a beast in her honor."

"No, that wouldn't work."

Now I knew that Fix was truly flustered. He was seriously considering my suggestions.

"Maybe I shouldn't even go to the funeral."

"Fix, if you do not attend, then you truly are a coward."

"I know you're right. It must be so easy for you."

"I may lead the life of a warrior, but it does not make the death of a comrade any easier. I remember when I lost one of my brothers in war we waged against the Goblin Hordes. He was killed in a rockslide. A terrible way to die. While the rest of my kinsman held feasts in his memory, I would not participate. There was only vengeance and fire in my heart. That week I slew a thousand Goblin Warmakers and a hundred Goblin Warlords. But their deaths still left me empty and wanting."

"What did you do?"

"I led an expedition to Hel and brought him back from the Land of the Dead. He's doing quite well now."

Alas, my tale did not seem to help Fix. He looked vexed.

"Ya know, Sven," he said half smiling. "You're advice doesn't always apply, but its always wrapped up in a really cool story."

CHAPTER 10 (Goda): The Wolf in Prison Gray

I don't normally do jumpers. I figure, if a guy wants to off himself without harassing the rest of the world, more power to 'em. Guess that's kind of cold, coming from a homicide detective, but hey— I got twenty-three years on the force and nothing to show for it but a ten million dollar peg leg. I got my own problems.

"Sorry to make you come out here, Lieutenant Goda," Buchanon apologized routinely. "Our jumper's not jumpin'. He's already dead."

"What did he fall up? How the fuck did he die?"

Buchanon was a bridge cop. Drove back and forth across the same piece of asphalt for eleven years. Great guy, boring as shit. Had a way of taking too long to tell me things.

"One of the repair crew doesn't show up for work. Boss figures he's sick. Then one of the crew notices his car still parked in the lot from last night. On their way up, they find his hard hat and spot his arm dangling over the ledge."

"What's the body doin' up there? Get it down."

"Can't. Not without destroying evidence. His blood is all over up there. We figured it might be your Flayer."

I raised an eyebrow at Buchanon. He gave me the same gesture I get from underage kids drinking beer. That's all I need for the press to start callin' my perp "The Flayer". Wind the sick fuck up and have him kill ten more people or drive him underground so it takes five years for him to show his face again.

"You're the only one that can get up there without ruining the evidence. The rescue crew doesn't figure it's worth the risk with all this wind."

Normally, this kind of high-profile gig woulda been reserved for one of the Liberators. They get one of their muscle-bound lummoxes dressed in a speedo and a cape to fly up there and catch the jumper at the last second. Top story, six o'clock news. Enough good PR to choke a publicist. Except this job just happened to be baggin' and taggin' a corpse, so naturally they all just happened to be "busy". I was the closest thing to "super" on the bridge, so I guess I was stuck with it. Never fear, Tommy Goda's here.

"All right, get these people back and tell the rescue crews to stand by."

I got a boot from one of the workmen. They had magnets in the soles for better traction. My leg didn't do much, but it did come with a powerful magnet in the heel.

Turning away from the crowd, I consulted my owner's manual. I could adjust the strength of the magnet with a simple turn of a screw. If things got too windy up there, all I had to do was stamp my foot and I wouldn't be goin' anywhere. Well, at least the Leg wouldn't.

"Hey, you okay?" asked Buchanon.

Guess I was startin' to show a little wear.

"Yeah," I said with trepidation. "I just got that creepy chill down the back of my neck. Like the first time I saw one of Carl's victims."

Buchanon took a step back. I was a little surprised, but I guess I was too punchy to realize what I was sayin'. Even in homicide, you don't take serial killers casually, especially ones like Carl. I still have the nightmares.

"He's locked away, Tommy," said Buchanon somberly. "You don't think—"

"Don't say it, Buch. For Jesus sake, don't even *think* it. I'll see ya in a few."

The first few hundred feet are a cinch. The noise of the cars and people fade away, until it's just me, the Delaware River and a three-hundred-foot drop. The Pacto Hi-Speed Line rumbles away from Jersey and who could blame it? Finally, I near the top of the bridge. Nice place to dump a body, if you can fly.

Just as I'm about to pull myself to the top of the bridge span, when the Leg slips of a tiny river of blood. Guess the eggheads at the cybernetics lab didn't account for this scenario. I pound my heel just in time. Unfortunately, I'm left over-extended between the lip of the top of the bridge span and the spot where I finally stamped my foot.

I hold there for a few seconds, mentally going through the owner's manual in my head. Then I remember another feature. Slipping off the workman's boot, I use my good toe to push a hidden button on the Leg. It extends and pushes me high enough so I can climb to the top.

The first thing I see is a hand and that's all I see. The poor bastard is everywhere. After I climb up and get my footing, I have to shake something off my arm. It was red and it was soft and let's leave it at that.

Shooing away the seagulls, I take a few pictures of the crime scene. Between the wind and the fucking birds, there isn't much of a crime scene. The victim's rib cage was busted open like a piñata. It coulda been the Flayer, Carl or Jeffrey Dahmer for all I knew.

Looking down across the river, I spot the prison and decide to walk the bridge span down the other side toward Jersey. Half way down, I make eye contact with this prisoner. Standing in the middle of the yard, which was once the baseball field for the cons, he stands looking up at me. Despite the distance, I'm almost sure he makes eye contact. Weird thing is, he isn't wearing the fashionable "shoot-me orange". He's still in old prison gray .

I take it as a sign that I should visit. The murder, the M.O. and the location are just too damn close to Carl for me to pass it off as coincidence. Maybe I was being paranoid, but when I got down to my car, I loaded my gun with the special armor piercers. If Carl was somehow getting out, I don't imagine it would take him long to find me or Tina and the kids. That was my waking nightmare.

As I drove toward New Jersey, the dream continued to play in my mind. I pictured a grassy knoll, birds chirping, trees blowin' in the breeze and the name "Carl Cannon" engraved across a tombstone.

<u>CHAPTER 11</u> (Mark): What's There to Like about Funerals?

You know you're getting old when you can't get out of a funeral. Teens and under, its easy. In the twenties, I was away at college half the time. But now, in the twilight of my second decade, I actually know the stiff. There's something there and I don't like it.

That was the one thing Viv and I had in common. We both hated funerals. She would've hated the funeral home her family picked out. Very traditional. Boring old oak paneling, people crying and sad, sad music.

"When I die, Fix," she used to say. "I want fireworks and naked Chippendales and jello shots. I want people to play quarters off my forehead and do lines on my coffin lid! It will be an absolute blast, my funeral!"

Yeah, the dead talk big. But when the relatives take over, the grief button goes into override. I'm not goin' out that way. I'm gonna be frozen. Just pop me in the freezer next to Walt. See you in a millennium suckers!

After a hellish morning of trying to find a dark tie, the Nippon rumbled into the funeral home parking lot. Today's soundtrack is *Dark Side of the Moon* from Floyd. Perfect for funerals, suicides or watching new episodes of SNL. My head was pounding like I just came from a Gwar concert and I was praying my over-the-counter cold medicine was enough to blanket my brain in sweet numb. Then I spotted Phil and flagged him down for a pep talk.

"Hey, buddy."

"W'sup, Mark. Unbelievable, huh?"

"Yeah, its weird. I mean— Did you see Mindy?"

"She's taking it hard, Mark. You're gonna be there for her."

In my circle of friends, Phil was not the richest, nor the smartest. He was by no means, the coolest, the poorest, the most pathetic or the most famous. However, when it came to emotional crisis such as this, he was Commander in Chief. The Shoulder Supreme. I deferred to his great wisdom.

"I'll catch you later, man," I said in acknowledgment.

"Good luck, Mark."

I gently pushed myself through the sea of sad faces. I was going to avoid the coffin pass if I could. I've got kind of a "Klingon attitude" when it comes to the body. Secretly,

I was wishing Viv was here to organize. It would've been a lot more fun, even if she did make fun of my furniture.

I found Mindy in the back room with the rest of her clique. If you needed more proof that gorgeous women hang together, it was right in that room.

There was Angeline. Kind of a dicey blonde lawyer with legs you'd slit your own throat for. Snazzy business suit and a permanent cigarette hanging out of her mouth. Angeline was kind of their hero. Strong, independent, tough as Kevlar, and no man to speak of.

Denise was just plain evil. At home, she was the perfect mother with one point two kids, a house and a husband. (I list it that way because that's the way she would. Here's my car, my hair dryer, my husband, my bikini wax...) Get her in this group and it was like she never left the sorority. Pills and JD, blackjack til five AM and run home just in time to yell at Mr. Denise.

Always in the center, was Mindy. The girls doted on her. She was their project, their protégé'. Each trying to mold Mindy in her image, as they tried with Viv. But like all children, Viv and Mindy resisted and the group eventually decided to cut their losses and stick with Mindy, much to their chagrin today.

Finally, there was Shelly. My sweet beautiful mistake. She oozed sex appeal like an overflowing tube of suntan oil. Shelly was a model and with good reason. Anything draped over that Italian bad girl bod was hot. You know how Italian girls look really hot between sixteen and twenty-one, then balloon past the point of no return? Not Shelly. Her biological gears jammed at seventeen and man — even here, even now — as much as I wanted to be there for Mindy. I looked at her and prayed to God her eyes didn't answer back.

"Hey, babe," I said, looking toward Mindy hopefully.

Her clique reluctantly parted for me. My decade of history was as much with them as it was with Mindy. Besides, I was the boyfriend now and had to play the part. Mindy looked at me, with tears welling. I almost half expected her to throw me out, but she just hugged me. She gave me that desperate, "thank-God-you're-here" hug that was worth more than any accepted apology.

"Mindy, I'm so sorry," I whispered. "About everything. I've been such a jerk."

"It doesn't matter," she assured. "I'm just glad you're here."

Mindy gestured for the rest of the group to leave, as if I had passed some silent, sorority security test. Angeline offered me a valium, but I declined. The relief that Mindy wasn't going to start screaming at me in the middle of her best friend's funeral was thanks enough.

"We need to talk, Mark. I need you to do me a favor."

Wow! Not only do I jump right back into my previous vaunted boyfriend position, but I get an opportunity to endear myself to Mindy even more. If I wasn't at a funeral, I'd say this was a pretty good day.

"Sure, babe. You'd know I'd do anything for you."

Mindy took on this very grim and sober look. Kind of like Rambo before he stormed the P.O.W. camp.

"You can find the person who did this. You find them and kill them."

Anyone see my jaw? I think it's on the floor.

"Mindy, you're upset and—"

"Don't patronize me!"

Uh, I could use that valium now.

"Mindy, calm down."

This whole thing was blowing up in my face. I was trying to guide Mindy into a back room because her screaming was surely audible in the coffin room just behind me. People started to look down the hall. I looked around nervously; half-embarrassed, half-angry.

"You find who did this! You kill 'em or we're through," she insisted.

"Are you nuts? I'm not killing anyone, besides, I can't interfere with a police investigation. God," I whispered in exasperation.

"You did it before!"

That was it. I shoved Mindy into the back room. Great, not only am I arguing with her at a funeral, I actually had to get physical. I actually had to physically fight with her to get her out of hearing range of the rest of the mourners. I'm in a nightmare, here.

"That is not for public knowledge," I hissed. "That was a secret, Min'. One of our secrets! God!"

I have never hit Mindy in anger. Not ever. Nor would I, but at that moment, I just felt so betrayed. There are secrets and there are secrets. This was *the* secret. It took me a month to get over just telling her.

"Well, is it any different?" she asked, finally lowering her voice. "Is it any different than what happened with Gordo?"

"That was *completely* different," I hissed.

"Why? Because he was your friend? You never liked Viv, admit it!"

"Mindy, it was different with Gordo. If I had stopped— Had time to think about it— You don't know what you're asking!"

"I don't care! I don't care! You find 'em and you kill 'em! If we mean anything to each other, you do it! Just—"

Mindy just pooped out right there, in mid-sentence, emotionally drained. There was just no reasoning with her right now. I guided her back to her clique praying she get hold of her senses before she blurted something out we'd both never live down.

And yes, once, a long time ago, I killed somebody. I'd rather not get into now, thank you very much. Suffice it to say, it was all very justified and my secretary won't be back in ten minutes.

The rest of the funeral was just as dull and traditional as you might expect. After everyone left the coffin room, I snuck back in with the undertakers to say my own good-bye.

"You got a cigarette?" I asked one of them.

He quickly offered me a smoke, as he tried to gather up the flowers. I gestured for his partner not to close the lid and stuck the cigarette in Viv's mouth. It was a token gesture, but somehow, somewhere, I knew she'd appreciate it.

"Good-bye, dah-ling."

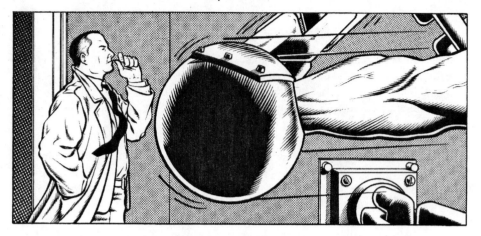

CHAPTER 12 (Goda): And Carl is Growing

The warden nearly popped a gasket when I made the request, but Carl was my collar, so what was he gonna do?

"Lieutenant, I can assure you," he intoned, trying to stay polite. "Carl Cannon hasn't moved from his cell since his appeal papers were filed. If he had, I don't think I'd be talking to you right now. I made his list."

Carl had tried to kill so many people during his reign of terror, we found a list on him with fifty names. Only seven of the names don't currently appear on tombstones.

"Look, I can sympathize with your position, warden."

"Oh, really? And how many prisons have you run, Lt. Goda? Everytime we so much as move Carl, the other prisoners act up. They think he's going to tear the place down and he probably would if he ever got loose."

"Warden, I got a murder investigation that's going nowhere. I got a murderer whose M.O. matches Carl. I have to know for myself."

I took a chance on the warden. If he made Carl's list, we had something in common.

"I have nightmares, warden," I confided. "I'll have them everyday until I know he's dead. You ever talk to the scientists that come in here and examine Carl?"

The warden sighed wearily and looked away.

"Five minutes and I cannot guarantee your safety."

"Make it ten and don't worry," I assured him. "Deep down, Carl's just another punk."

I went through processing to get to Carl's cell. Having already given up my gun at the front door, I now had to pull off the leg. No weapons of any kind was the rule and, uncomfortable as that made me, I hopped on.

The hallway to Carl's cell had four doors. Two had manual keys and two had computer locks, which were changed with every guard shift. Two armed guards were stationed on either side of the door to Carl's room. They had orders to shoot anyone without a pass or Carl, if he somehow managed to get this far.

The door to Carl's cell was a four-foot thick safe door, with titanium bolts to hold it in place. (The prisoners called it the Carl Savings and Loan. Mainly because of the door, but also because Carl promised payback with interest.) The combination on the lock was changed weekly. There was a short, five-foot diameter hallway, too small for Carl to get inside and then, Carl's room.

The room was about fifty feet square, with a thirty-foot high ceiling. No windows and ten-foot thick walls. Carl sat in the center on a chair made from cinderblocks. Huge chains, with links as thick as a man, crisscrossed him in every direction. His arms and legs each had a chain that ran to a two-ton winch just outside the room. They used it to forcibly move Carl to one side of the room.

The biggest chain was connected to his waist and a twelve-ton cement block which made up the floor of the room. Finally, his hands had been encased in steel balls, making it impossible for him to grip anything or anyone. The only light was from some bare bulbs that hung just out of Carl's reach, not that he could really see it. His head was encased in a helmet, which was heat resistant and let in very little ambient light. If he got it off, one look and I'd be toast.

When I caught Carl, he was a little over seven feet, now he was an easy twelve feet. His massive arms and legs were like tree trunks and his head was as big as a dog house.

And Carl is growing.

"Whattaya say, Carl?" I began, flipping a toothpick into my mouth. "They let you go to the bathroom or do you just shit your drawers all day?"

You never get over it. You would not believe how something that big can move that fast. Carl was across the room in less time that it took me to bite down on the toothpick. Every chain stretched to its maximum and I could hear the block in the center of the room shift in its space. I was about three feet out of Carl's grasp and he swung his arms hard enough to kick up a decent breeze.

"Carl, I don't have time to fuck with you today."

I put on a pretty good front for a guy about to shit his own drawers.

"I'll kill you, Goda! Your family! Your friends! Everyone you ever *met*!"

"You know, your little hissy fit might work for the eggheads they have examining you, but to me, you're just another piece of shit."

Almost losing my balance, I grabbed one of the low hanging lightbulbs, busted the bulb and jammed the jagged end to one of the chains. The lights dimmed in half the county and Carl got a little preview of the electric chair. He screamed and fell to the floor. I could smell the hair burning.

"I got some more questions for ya, genius," I added.

"Go fuck yourself."

"Wrong answer."

I juiced him again. A viewscreen on the outside of his helmet came to life as he sat up and gave me that dirty look I know so well in my dreams.

"What do you want?" he rumbled.

"There was a murder on top of the Ben Franklin two nights ago. You do it?"

Carl made an attempted to hold his belly and laughed for probably the first time in years. His chains rattled and the walls shook.

"Goda, there's a lot of people I want to kill. You, the guards, that perky chick from Murphy Brown— You think I grew a brain in here? You think I've had time to master some subtle mind games to play on the guards and you? If I get out of here Goda, it'll be god damn global news, man. It'll be like a fucking bomb went off! Bodies piled high— Hell, I'll kill the *trees*. The doctors say I'm gaining an inch a week. By Christmas, this room won't be able to hold my *dick*."

Whatever biohazard Carl fell into, it was wreaking havoc with his genes. He got bigger and more powerful by the minute. By the time his lawyers appeal his death sentence, he'll be as big as a skyscraper. Half the eggheads that were examining him were studying ways just to kill him. Somehow, I didn't think the world's shittiest superman was going to sit still for them.

"So you don't know anything about the bridge murder?"

"No."

Up to that point, I thought I was wasting my time. As a trained observer of scumbags, I've come to rely on speech patterns and body movements as indicators of truth. Carl liked to ramble, unless he was lying, in which case, he answered in short, abrupt answers, hoping I'd change the subject.

"No?"

"Yeah."

"Why are you lying, Carl?"

"Fuck you."

"You're actually afraid of something."

Unbelievable. Carl had his own kryptonite. I jammed the wire into the chain. Carl agonized again, but this time he seemed determined to take the pain. He banged his helmet against the floor of the cell, trying to crack the visor.

"Fuck you, Goda! Whattaya gonna do? Kill me now?! You had your chance, asswipe!"

I pulled out a jar-sized container I had smuggled past the guards.

"You're right and I've regretted it, but all I could get past the guards was this."

I tossed the jar to Carl. It's contents spilled all over him and right down his crotch.

"What the fuck?!"

"That's the strongest itching powder money can buy. Amazing stuff. I put it down my brother's back last Christmas. He still has the rash. I'll get you the antidote if you tell me your little secret."

Carl started shaking like crazy. He rubbed the steel balls against himself in vain.

"You can't do this! This is cruel and unusual!"

"You're cruel and unusual, you should feel right at home."

"Make it stop! Make it stop!"

"What do you know, Carl?"

"All right, all right! One of the other prisoners— Been here forever— They call 'em Wolf. He saw what happened on the bridge."

"He's a witness? How do you know?"

"They send some of the prisoners in here to bathe me and wipe my ass. They overheard him in the yard."

"This Wolf— Black hair, gray overalls?"

"I don't know! C'mon, man!"

"I didn't mean to rush you. I'll come back."

"No! He— Some of the older prisoners— I heard them call him Lucky, once. He wears sunglasses, that's all I know! Now get me the antidote!"

"I'll be right back," I smiled. "As soon as they invent one."

"GODAAAAAAAAA!!"

This was turning into a bad day for everyone, but me. The prisoners went nuts when the lights dimmed. When I got outside, the warden was in the middle of a lock down.

He'd be pissed as Hell when I told him I wanted a tour of the prison to look for Lucky. He sat me in an empty visitors room for my own protection, while I tried to reattach the Leg. The warden hissed something about bringing me up on charges, but I didn't take him too seriously. Carl or me would be dead before the issue got brought in front of a judge. Just as I got the leg reattached and reached for my pants, a prisoner in gray pressed a sharpened shiv against my neck.

"Don't move, flatfoot. Or you'll be whistling outta yer lar-y-nex. Heard yous was lookin' for da Wolf."

"Word travels fast in a prison riot."

"Don't it? I'll answer your questions, but you don't turn around and you don't see my face. Capish?"

"Why?"

"I gotta live here. I wish to keep my an-no-nim-i-ty."

"Put the shiv away."

"Just ask your questions."

"All right, what did you see?"

"I gotta cell dat overlooks da river. Nicest bunk in da Joint. Coupla nights ago, I'm lookin' up there and I see two mooks in a fight."

"This was at night?"

"Yeah, will yous let me finish?"

"How could you see anything at that distance?"

"I got good night vision, it runs in da family! Jesus Christ, just let me finish!"

While Wolf rambled, I stole a glance at one of the doors and caught a glimpse of him in the reflection. He looked like just another paisan with a hair helmet and shades. But he was too young to hold any clout in a place like this. And sunglasses in prison were about as common as priests in an adult bookstore.

"So the one guy, his hands turn into knives or somethin'. Chopped the other mook into pat-te' and ripped out his liver."

"Knives, huh?"

"Yeah. What? Like you ain't watched the news? These Liberators do that shit in their sleep now."

"Did he dress like a Liberator?"

"Naw, normal guy. On the big side, though. He looked like that football player. That mul-en-yam from Brentwood."

"I think you're watchin' too much CNN."

"Hey. Ya ever wonder they can't convict the sonuvabitch? Think about it."

"Why would he come all the way to Philly to—"

"I don't fuckin' know and I don't care. All I said was dat he *looked* like da mook. Dat good enough fer yous?"

"You make a lot of threats for a guy in the joint."

"Yeah, well I play dis place like a fiddle. I got ten guys that'll stick you for half a pack of Luckies. So don't get any ideas about findin' me. I'm vapor, ya understand?"

"Listen, calm down. I'm not after you. Here, have a—"

I turned to offer him a smoke, but he was already out of the room without a sound. Just like vapor.

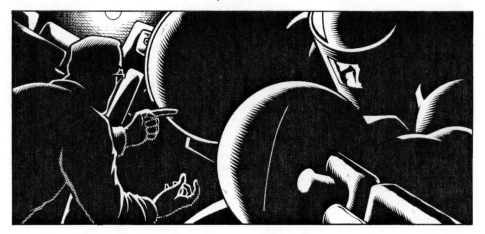

CHAPTER 13 (Narrator): Interlude with the Werewolf

Long after Goda left the prison and the lock down gave way to the uneasy dreams of prisoners, Carl stirred in his massive chair. He had only slept for ten minutes, but that was usually enough to take him through the week now. He squinted at the inside of his visor, searching for a hairline crack. That's when he felt the door open and the air in the room shift.

"You forget your leg, Goda?" laughed Carl, looking up.

There was no reply, except the steady, deliberate, footsteps of someone approaching from the dark. He walked underneath the only light bulb left in the room. He was in striking distance, but before Carl pounced, he realized who it was.

"Seventy-five years," said the Wolf in disgust. "Seventy-five fucking years I've waited to get out of this can, Carl. Ya stupid fuck."

There were only three times in his life that Carl Cannon had been scared. The first was when his father hung him out a window by the ankles when he was six. The second was when he fell into a vat of experimental, genetic material at the lab when he was sweeping up. And the third, which was the worst, was the day he met the Wolf.

"N-now, n-now, L-lucky—-"

The name made the Wolf even more incensed.

"Ya see? That's what I'm talkin' about! No one calls me Lucky no more, Carl! No one! No one knew who I was until you talked ta dat cop! Seventy-five years I waited!"

"B-b-but-but—-"

"I coulda walked outta here wit total an-no-nim-ity! Seventy-five years of planning ruined by a giant medigan!"

The Wolf strode forward, as Carl shrank away. He put his finger against a small area on Carl's head not covered by the helmet.

"I'm s-s-sorry, Luc— Wolf. Don't worry, I can get you out of here right now. Just loosen my chains a little."

"Let *you* out? You brainless fuck!" Wolf half laughed. "I'm gonna own this city inside a week when I get out and you just don't fit into da scheme o' things. Ya a-bom-min-a-tion."

Wolf had long since been able to control his transformation. Even now, a full moon would only make him a little restless, if that was all he wanted. But when his ire went up, his razor stubble grew a little hairy and his teeth turned into a maw of fangs. Before Carl could think of another excuse, Wolf let his finger transform into a pointed claw, which popped through Carl's head like a hole punch. Wolf pulled his finger out, as Carl's lifeless body slumped to the floor. He tasted the blood.

"Hmm. I think you're a quart low," he quipped.

The Wolf strolled out the room. He started to whistle "Mack the Knife", but stopped in mid-song, growling in frustration. He only had a few months left on his sentence, but that cop knew.

"Seventy-five years," he growled.

<u>CHAPTER 14</u> (Mark): Stones & Atigo on a Sunday Afternoon

I was in a bad funk when I got back to the office. My headache didn't bother me, but I felt sleepy as Hell. The address on this place oughta be Catch-22. It's the only place where I can do business, but I never feel like doing business while I'm here. I know I should be paying my rent, calling a lawyer about facing Mrs. Porter in court and generally tidying up, so as to not completely disgust potential clients. I slipped out of my funeral gear and slipped into jeans and a concert shirt for an Irish, funkadelic band called "Get Jack's Drink".

I tried going home, but that's no place for concentrated thinking. First mom starts grilling me about the funeral, then dad notices his car could use a wash. The next thing you know, I'm moving stuff into the attic and getting into arguments about why I've never liked fish for dinner. I gotta get my own place.

All I end up doing is sitting in the office, listening to the Stones and playing Mushroom King IV on my Atigo GS all day. Two secret worlds later and I'm still in a funk. All I can think about is Mindy and mindlessly jumping computer animated mushrooms.

Briefly, I turn on the TV. The ex-quarterback of Philadelphia, Cory Rothinger, was being interviewed about how he can be a sucky quarterback for his new team, twelve states away. (Here in South Jersey, we have a love/hate relationship with the Philadelphia teams, which is usually put aside to fully hate the Austin Rangers.) Then, the local news did yet another fluff piece on the Philadelphia Liberators. It's amazing what suckers the Media are for a flashy, red, white & blue costume and anyone holding the title "superhero". Most of the ones I met were real assholes, except Sven, of course. Although his friend, Hector was pretty cool, now that I think about it. You'd know Hector better as Hector Vector, the lightning man. They ought to call him the Hector Hashish for all the pot he smokes.

By the time I'm done watching TV, it's dark outside the office. Even the skate punks are heading home for the evening and I'm still paralyzed with indecision. I could find the guy who killed Viv. One sip of the Stuff and I'd have everything but his driver's license number. But I shouldn't kill him. Should I? Maybe if I just look for him, I'll get lucky and he'll try and kill me.

What am I saying?!

Jesus in a jeep, she's going to drive me right to the nut house.

I pick up the phone and punch the auto-dial button marked "Aldo". Aldo is my mysterious benefactor. He started calling me a few years ago. Sometimes with a case, sometimes with a lead on a case. He's kind of like my own private Charlie to my Angels. Although, aside from the smug satisfaction he gets from steering me in the right direction, he never seems to get anything out of it.

"It's me," I greet curtly.

"Ah, Fix, my man of mystery," he says flamboyantly. "Investigator of Interesting Intrigue, Ender of Enigmas, Master of—"

"What do you get paid by the hour? Shut up and listen to me already. I need some information on a homicide. You ever hear of the Flayer?"

"Yeah, interesting stuff," he says, as I can hear him tap on a keyboard vigorously. "Bunch of weird murders, mostly in Philly. Too much to tell you on the phone, you want it now or should I send it snail mail?"

"Better fax it, I think my Internet account is overdue."

"Well, I hope you got a roll of new fax paper, because it is a monstrous case file. Fascinating autopsy photos too. Not to pry, but, are you all right, Fix? You haven't even tried to trick me into revealing my location."

It was kind of a contest with me and Aldo. He'd call or I'd call and then I try and get a fix on him. Usually it's pretty amusing to see what part of the world he'd route his calls through, but today, I just don't have the energy.

"I'm just not myself tonight. One of Mindy's friends is the victim, so this is all a little close to home."

"I see," he said, genuinely sympathizing. "So you're just looking over the case. You're not actually investigating."

"Are you nuts? You know what kind of trouble I'd be in?"

Thirty minutes later, I'm wondering what the Hell I'm doing in Viv's neighborhood. It's bad enough the Philly PD doesn't like me and here I am to personally step on Lt. Goda's toes.

Viv's neighborhood was one of those trendy, North Philly crackhouse streets. Half yuppie rebuilders and half locals. Viv's condo complex was fenced in and decorated in early urban warfare and barbed wire. I left the Nippon around the corner near a row of headless parking meters. My "car alarm" consisted of locking the doors, a great deal of prayer and turning up the radio to full volume. I figure, if I got jacked, at least I'd scare the shit out of the guy before my car ended up in the auto parts shop.

The complex had a security door. You had to buzz someone inside in order to get let in. Some early twenties, "I'm-too-young-to-be-dressing-this-old" stockbroker type, walked blindly into the street, giving me ample time to skip out of the shadows and catch the door. I shoulda mugged him just to teach him a lesson.

Viv lived on the eighth floor. The police tape was still on the door, as if yellow plastic strip were a threat to evidence tamperers and crime junkies. No, really, some people get off on this crime stuff. I knew this guy in college. Used to listen to the police bands and sneak into crime scenes after the fact. He finally got caught when a detective went back to a scene for his umbrella. Found him masturbating in the bathroom. I never understood the masturbating part. Oh, well, back to reality.

I was standing in Viv's hall looking over my lock-picking tools. Some moron down the hall was blasting "Achy, Breaky Heart" at a decibel level that was well beyond any sensible listening volume, which brought my headache back. None of this helped me, since I'm already the world's worst lock pick.

All the training I know, I downloaded from the Internet. Oh, sure, it's good for easy things, like bombs and porn, but something as subtle as lock-picking. Feh. I don't have the patience anyway. After about three minutes of bending my little tools, I go for the back up— One of Mindy's credit cards.

Hey, if I had one, I'd use mine.

Of course, just as soon as I get it in the door jam, "Achy Breaky..." goes up fifty decibels, as the redneck yuppie down the hall opens the door. I would've booked and ended my whole investigation right there, but I panicked and Mindy's card slipped inside. Eye contact is made with Ms. Redneck Yuppie. She's throwing a party and looks at me with disdain.

"Yes?" she stops to ask on her way to another apartment.

"Um, I, uh, left a jacket in there," I apologize. "You know, I didn't want to disturb the family..."

"Yeah, well, she's dead."

Brrrrr, cold in here.

"Uh, yeah, very tragic. Were you close?"

"No."

I had one more sentence to enlist her help. You can just tell by the concentrated speech pattern. If I could just ask and respond in short, concise sentences, she might just be not that annoyed enough to help me. She was in the adjoining apartment and I remembered that Viv's balcony was pretty close to her neighbor's.

"Get me in? Balcony?"

"Uh," she substituted for, "Are you kidding?"

"It's a really nice jacket. Like Kramer's on *Seinfeld*."

She had listened too long, now she had to help me.

"Help me with the ice," she said, exasperated beyond belief.

She led me into a stranger's apartment, then leaves me to crush some ice in her neighbor's sink. Her neighbor, who's never seen me before, walks out of his bedroom in a daze. I turn to him, ice pick in hand. He nods, like it's the most natural thing in the word to see a total stranger in your kitchen with an ice pick.

I must be in the most unsafe condo on the planet. I'm surprised the killer didn't just go floor by floor murdering each oblivious yuppie. Then again, people always act weird at a party. Especially if they're networking.

"You from C.J.'s?" asks dazed and confused.

"Yeah," I reply with the simplest answer.

"What's your whole take on the Winston merger?"

"Well, the Winston merger," I scoff, as if he should know, even though I don't. "You know what I'm sayin'?"

"Oh, absolutely."

Good, now explain it to me.

"Personally, I've always suspected the deal went down two weeks ago during the initial meeting," he whispers to me intently.

Um, I was just chipping ice...

"They say Claymore *cleaned* up."

"No!" I say aghast.

Who the fuck is Claymore?

"Got his wife to buy up shares before the announcement. I mean, c'mon, how long before he has to pay for that, right?"

"Hey, that's what *I'm* saying."

Jesus in a jumpsuit! Get me out of this conversation!

"Let's go," says the woman, reappearing with a cigarette.

I scoop up my ice. Dazed and confused is sorry to see me go and wants to keep in touch.

"Ice," I say, overly gesturing my exit.

"Oh, by the way, I'm Nicholas Turner. See you at the office, uh..."

"Terry Frenzen...fin," I mumble lamely.

Yeah, try and find me.

"Nice talkin' to ya."

Before the hostess changes her mind, I walk inside with the ice, plunk it on the bar and walk straight out onto the balcony. I step across to Viv's before anyone can comment. Don't mind me, just breaking into your neighbor's place.

Viv's place is a mess. I got a friend who tried to talk me into a crime scene clean up business, but I don't think I could do it. Not that blood bothers me, per se, but I'd start wondering who died, what happened, etc, etc. Fix can't resist a mystery. I'm sorta like Fred on Scooby-Doo. I avoid the dried puddle of blood and look around. The dining room table still had a stack of mail. Victoria's Secret catalogue, which I took for further study, some unpaid bills and a postcard from one of those labs that tests medicine on human subjects. Guess Viv was a little desperate for cash.

I tried to remember if Mindy had ever mentioned she was broke (a topic of conversation I usually tune out). Unfortunately, I can still hear the country music next door, so I turn on the stereo to drown it out. She left the stereo switched to the tape player and I decide to check out Viv's music tastes.

It's the Beatles and "Run for your Life".

"I didn't know you were a Beatles fan," I say to Viv's chalk outline.

I fart around the apartment looking for clues, not that it really mattered. The Stuff would steer me to the killer. Then I realized, the song started over. I go over and forward the tape. It's homemade and that's all that's on it. "Run for your Life" over and over again.

Then it occurs to me, the only thing Viv ever listened to in her car was Mariah Carey and Whitney Houston. She didn't have enough taste to listen to the Fab Four. I remember a tortuous ride from the airport where all she played was that fucking "Bodyguard" soundtrack over and over. If I get sent to Hell, that airport ride is waiting for me.

Carefully, I slip the tape out without touching it and drop it into a lower pocket in my trenchcoat. Once I find the killer, I'd need some proof that he'd been here.

Now for some answers. I drink the Stuff.

It's hard to describe what its like. Taste like shit, that's for sure. I'm gagging and coughing, hoping I don't burst into flame or grow an extra leg out of my head. It's always something different every time I take it, but a few things stay the same.

Fog billows in from nowhere. My eyes and mouth glow a bright green, like my head's some sort of day glow jack o' lantern. Then I get the Visions. It's like trying to watch one-hundred TV channels at the same time, while listening to every radio station, while eating every frozen food entree' the supermarket has to offer, and smelling every armpit in the State of New Jersey. Total sensory overload. My brain can't even process it all.

I see visions of the past, present and future. I'm in twelfth grade and Mindy turns me down for a date for the first time. I'm standing in a graveyard early today, watching them lower Viv's casket into the ground. It's forty years from now, I'm standing on South Street looking up at a wanted poster with Mindy's picture on it. She's old and she's wearing my hat.

I hear horns, dogs barking, Homer saying "D'oh!" and the whispering of wind. I taste pizza sauce, blood, clam juice, and Castle Burger's apple pie. I smell fresh cut grass, burning rubber, garlic, and perfume. I feel denim, stucco, and cold flesh.

Then just as I think my head's going to spin around and break off my neck, it comes into focus. There's no sound, but Viv's standing at the Jacuzzi and I'm watching her through the eyes of the killer. Something happens and then she's lying dead. The killer is holding her liver and in the reflection in the stereo lid, I see him. It's Victor.

<u>CHAPTER 15</u> (Goda): Feds don't say Thanks

I never understood the way movies portray cops. They get all upset when feds show up and take a case off their hands. Me? I almost danced a jig when Agents Mass and Keystone walked in. Like I need another super powered fuck up to put me on his list.

"Lieutenant," began Mass flashing his I.D. "Agent Mass and this is Keystone. We'll be taking the Flayer investigation from here."

"I got all the files right here," I said proudly.

I put a bible-sized stack of papers in front of the suits.

"Where'd he cross the state line?" I asked.

"I'm sorry, that information's classified," assured Keystone. "I understand you worked on the Carl Cannon case."

"Well, you can say that, I put the scumbag behind bars."

I couldn't tell if they were impressed are just surprised.

"Where are your copies?"

"Well, the duty sergeant gets a copy, one goes to records and another copy gets filed here," I explained, gesturing to the homicide cabinets.

"We have the other copies. We'll need these and any others."

"S'okay with me, but you're gonna leave me a copy, right?"

I was trying to be polite, but these guy had some kind of problem with me. It was like me or the whole squad was beneath their notice.

"Excuse me?" said the tall one, emptying the homicide drawer.

"Well, I mean. Not that I want it, but you gotta leave us one copy, in case."

"In case what?"

"I don't know. Lawsuit or some bullshit. C.Y.A. right?"

Keystone and Mass looked at each other. I translated.

"Cover Your Ass."

"Lt. Goda, you have your orders, we have ours. Ours is to take everything related to the Flayer out of your hands. Everything. If you so much as mention anything connected to this case, we can have you brought up on charges of insubordination."

"What is this? I help you and you come in here and threaten me?"

Now I was pissed. Captain McLane walked into the room with a matching expression. Guess he'd already been through this.

"Tommy, just let them do what they've got to do," he advised.

"Well, what the fuck is it to show a little professional courtesy around here?" I lamented.

"You're way out of your league, gentlemen." Keystone, the smart-ass said that.

McLane focused his eyes on Keystone, then shoved him up against the filing cabinets. Way to go Cap.

"Agent Keystone, you may have jurisdiction over our case and you may even have the right to be rude and obnoxious to us poor *local* cops. But just remember one thing."

Cap took his hand, the one with the glove on it, and opened Keystone's jacket. He took out his gun and crushed the barrel like it was made from wax. Keystone's mouth dropped opened.

"Cyber cops are in *everybody's* league. Good night, Tommy. I'll see you tomorrow."

I laughed and McLane walked away. I woulda bought Cap a beer, but he wasn't the social type. Neither am I, come to think of it, but I had to pay homage to his cojones.

On the way home I call Tina. She's ecstatic that I'm actually coming home before three AM, adding, "You might even get to see one of the kids!" My wife. A sense of humor and a great ass. Who could ask for anything more? Then the radio squawks the address of one of the victims.

"Dispatch, this is Romeo-Foxtrot-Seven, repeat your twenty."

"We're on Eighteenth and Bainbridge on that little side street. That you Tommy? Over."

"Yeah, hey, Darryl. What's the story? Over."

"We were making a pass at your victim's place like you asked. There's some weird lights up there. And it looks like we have a Japanese male watching the building from a blue Hunsai. Over."

"I'm enroute, sit tight till I get there. Over."

Darryl and his partner, Vincent. Just another couple of patrol cops that drink too much coffee. Actually, Darryl used to date my cousin. They had a pretty good thing goin' until I lost the leg. My cousin got more hysterical than Tina at the hospital. They split and to this day I still feel responsible. Darryl's a trooper though. Never says a word. I stop and buy them burgers.

"Gentlemen," I greet them from my car. "Picked up a little mid-patrol snack for ya."

"Thanks, Tommy. You didn't have to do that," he reminds me.

I look at the Japanese guy. Clean car, clean suit and clean cut.

"He could be waiting for anybody. What about the lights?"

"They stopped as soon as you got here. You want us to go up?"

"Yeah... I guess..."

"Something wrong, lieutenant?" asks Vince.

"I don't know. It's something with green lights. Somebody just said something about green lights the other day. Jesus Christ, what was it?"

While I'm thinking aloud, a call comes over the radio. A gang of kids is chasing somebody. Ever since that Polec kid died, the Philly PD has jumped on every teen violence call, as if it was the call to freakin' Armageddon.

"You okay with this, Tommy?" ask Darryl already starting his car.

"Go, go, it's probably nuthin'."

Darryl and Vince screeched away. I parked out of view of the Japanese guy just in case. In the darkness of a tree, I banged out a cigarette and tried to get one last light out of the Gipp lighter I should've replaced days ago. That's the worst part about smoking— Disposable lighters. You squeeze the thing for every last drop, then you feel like a junkie when it runs out on you and ya can't get it lit. I'm praying to God this dead broad's apartment has a gas stove, all because I didn't spend eighty-nine cents on a new plastic piece of shit. I'm bangin' the thing against the tree when I see 'em.

Quiet as wind, smooth as glass. The Japanese guy's friends pull up in a black Beamer with tinted windows. The only reason I heard anything was because the car doors snapped shut. Five other clean-cut Japanese guys get out of the car. They're carrying stainless steel knives and I don't mean the ones that have Ginsu on the side.

They're in the building faster than it takes for my cigarette to hit the ground. I got no time to call it in, so I run around the back. Whatever's going on, you can bet your ass it has to do with the green lights.

<u>CHAPTER 16</u> (Narrator): Manga Boys in the House

Fix was still tweaked on the Stuff when he called Mindy. Initially, she was skeptical, secretly thinking that Mark had made up the story about Victor in a futile attempt to teach her a lesson.

"Mindy, I'm telling you," Mark insisted. "I'm in Viv's place right now, I used the Stuff."

"Oh, you did that for me?" Mindy softened.

"I told you I'd do anything for you," Fix said back in his embarrassed schoolboy voice. "Except kill Victor, of course."

Then Mark heard Victor's voice call out from Mindy's adjoining room.

"Mindy? Is that Mark?"

"Don't worry," Mindy assured in a voice that terrified Mark. "You won't have to."

"No! No, Mindy! Wait!"

Simultaneously, Lt. Thomas Goda had run around back to the apartment building's courtyard, where the balconies faced. He squinted at the tiny instruction manual he kept in his hip pocket. His leg came with a tiny, calculator sized keyboard and screen. Tearing a hole in his pant leg, he opened it up and pushed the appropriate buttons. The leg could do everything he needed, save one. Judge the distance from the courtyard to the eighth floor balcony.

"Lessee. Eight stories, ceiling's about ten feet. Let's say ninety-two, including the ground floor."

And with that, Goda punched in "92" and leaned all his weight on his cybernetic prosthesis. One point three seconds later, the leg fired him skyward, perfectly arcing him towards Viv's balcony. Unfortunately, Goda failed to ad in the height of the balcony railing, which was another three feet. He grasped at the edge of the railing and struggled to pull himself up.

Mark immediately spotted him, but hesitated to go running to his aid. The Stuff was still working.

"Goda," he said trying to shield his eyes and redial Mindy. "What the Hell are you doing?"

"You're under arrest, Fix!"

Although Mark admired his tenacity, clearly, Goda was losing his grip. Letting him fall was out of the question, so he reached over the railing and offered his hand. Goda grabbed on, then stared back at Mark's eyes.

"Ah! What the fuck's wrong with you?!" demanded Goda.

"Oh, good, struggle with me. That'll help," growled Mark, pulling him over the railing.

"Jason— The green light— That's what I was trying to remember. You're a freak just like he said!"

"Look, you can't tell anybody about this."

"The Hell I can't!"

Just then, the door to Viv's apartment burst opened. Six very silent Japanese men entered, immediately cloaking themselves in shadow. Fix and Goda drew their guns.

"Where is Victor?" said the leader impatiently.

"Drop your weapons, I'm a cop."

"You did not answer my question."

"Uh, Goda, I don't think these— Gggg! Akkkk!"

Dropping his gun, Mark dropped to his knees, choking and grasping his throat. The Stuff had one more power to imbue upon him. Goda picked up Mark's gun and tried in vain to keep all the Japanese guys in his line of sight.

"You picked the wrong time to swallow a bug, Fix."

"By the time we are finished with you two," added the Japanese leader. "Neither one of you will be able to swallow much of anything. Now, where is Victor?!"

"Goda," gasped Fix. "Grab...onto...something."

"What?"

Mark couldn't hold back any longer. A roar that shatter Viv's windows and shook everyone else's for blocks, rocked the yuppie apartment complex. Strange bolts of green energy erupted from Mark's body, instantly burning holes through his clothes and bouncing around the room like mini balls of lightning. The clocks, lights and appliances went berserk. Viv's stereo surged to life, it's volume controls rolling to maximum and blasting "Rock N' Roll is Dead" by Lenny Kravitz. Fog billowed in the room from out of nowhere, but was blown away by a powerful surge of wind that impossibly emanated from Mark's windpipe.

Goda stamped his foot, locking the magnet against the base of the balcony's sliding door just in time. Two of the Japanese men were blown off the balcony, while the others were tossed about the room. When the wind subsided, Goda made his move. Grabbing Mark by the collar, he dragged the spent P.I. to his feet and they both stumbled out of the apartment.

"How did you do that?" asked Goda as he stumbled.

"If I knew that, I'd sell my gun," gasped Mark. "You got a breath mint?"

Three more uzi-wielding, Japanese thugs were just getting off the elevator in the hall. Goda and Mark immediately spotted them and made a break for the fire exit. Goda fired a shot, giving them a precious second to duck out of the way of the uzis' rain of death.

"Who are these guys?!" demanded Goda.

"The Manga Boys. Can I have my gun?"

"No."

At the top of the stairs, Mark grabbed a fire extinguisher. As the first Manga Boy came through, he hurled it down the stairs at him. Instinctively, he backed away, giving Goda and Mark enough time to turn the corner. By this time, the thugs in the apartment had also recovered and were in hot pursuit. The uzis were fired up through the next flight of stairs, but Goda and Mark managed to stay just inches in front of the bullets.

On the roof, Mark jammed the door shut with a screwdriver, while Goda looked around for an escape.

"Who the fuck are the Manga Boys?"

"They're Yakuza. 'Cept they got these really cool tattoos of Speed Lad and Astro Racer. Can I have my gun?"

"No, c'mon."

Goda looked at the roof to the building next store. It was lower and reasonably close to the apartment building.

"You want your gun, follow me," instructed Goda.

"Fuck no," said Mark immediately. "It's probably stuff like this, that got ya that leg."

Suddenly, the door to the roof was blasted away with a hail of bullets. Mark beat Goda to the next roof. Unfortunately, the Japanese thugs now had a better vantage point since they were on a higher roof. Mark and Goda dove behind a heavy looking air conditioning unit, while bullets landed around them. Goda gave Mark back his gun.

"Think your back up will be here sometime this *week*?!"

"Shut up, or I take yer gun back. Why don't you just zap 'em again?"

"Because the Stuff wore off!"

Goda returned fire, but could barely stick his head up to see. Mark watched two of the thugs jump to another roof. In a few seconds, they would be surrounded.

"We gotta get off of here," Mark stated.

"I'm open to suggestions."

Mark looked at the next building. They'd have to leap the distance of the width of the street and sidewalk to make the next roof.

"Jeez, how do the superheroes make these leaps?"

"Will you stop daydreamin' and return fire!"

"Oh, that's right, bat hook. Duh!" remembered Mark.

At this point, Goda was about to turn the gun on Mark. Fortunately, Mark came up with the solution.

"Think the leg can make it across this street?"

"Are you crazy? They'll shoot us as soon as we're airborne. Not to mention the fact I have no idea how to figure out the trajectory with you on board."

Mark fired a shot, slowing one of the Japanese thugs from getting to the third roof on their right.

"Well, I'm open to suggestions," mocked Mark.

Just as the lead Manga Boy signaled his two best men to make the leap to Mark and Goda's roof, Goda suddenly stood. He was facing away from the Mangas, with Mark slung over one shoulder. As Goda made the leap, Mark fired both guns at the Manga Boys. The twosome crashed through a skylight in a building across the street. Inside, their descent was broken by the branches of a tree, which was part of an indoor atrium. As police sirens met the ears of the remaining Manga Boys, they left as quickly and as silently as they arrived.

Mark and Goda slowly crawled from the pile of debris they had created. Alerted by the noise, an eighty-year old housesitter stood in the foyer of the next room, too stunned to do anything but listen to their conversation.

"C'mon, I know where Victor is."

"Now, hold up. What were you doing in there?"

"Does it matter? I know where Victor is and he's the killer."

"He's not the killer. The killer's a super."

"What? You're sure?"

"I wasn't at first. Had kind of an unreliable eyewitness. But when the feds took the case outta my hands, that's when I knew. And Victor's a normal guy, right?"

"Way below normal. Christ in a crockpot! We gotta go right now! If Victor's not the killer, he's probably our only witness and our only witness may be dead if we don't boogie. I swear, I'll explain on the way."

Mark spotted the old man.

"Hi," he said upon exiting.

CHAPTER 17 (Mindy): Mindy's Kitchen Nook of Death

Look, I don't care what Mark says. It was his fault. I wasn't really trying to kill Victor anyway. I mean, on the surface, it looked that way. But after Viv's funeral— And all that valium— I was in a weird mood.

"Mindy was that Mark? I really gotta talk to Mark," Victor pleaded, as he coughed.

"Mark will be here soon. Why don't you watch some TV?" I suggested, surprisingly calm for a rookie murderer. "You sound sick."

"I know, I'm wrecked. Thanks for letting me crash here," he repeated for about the tenth time. "I'm like, indebted."

Victor sat down next to Sniffles, my cat, and start flipping the TV. Sniffles snorted at him, shifted in his favorite part of the couch, then went back to sleep.

"What's wrong with your cat?"

"Deviated septum."

Victor was hoping to catch a news story about some drug kingpin he owed money. If the kingpin got caught before Victor did, he figured he could walk away scott-free. For a second, I felt sorry for him.

Then I remembered what Mark said he did to Viv. How I had to go identify my best friend in the morgue and how Victor didn't even show up at the funeral! He was a killer. I had to keep that in mind. For Viv's sake.

"Victor, you want something cold to drink?" I offered, continuing to pretend to be the perfect hostess.

"Sure, okay," he said half-heartedly. "Coke or something."

I opened the cabinet under the sink and pulled out the bottles of cleaners. It's where I keep the cleaning stuff, the baking soda and detergents. I could poison the bastard. That would be easy.

Paranoid about getting caught, I just threw a bunch of the stuff in a glass and tossed in some ice to make it look good. Unfortunately, it didn't look anything like soda or ice tea, so I decided to pour some diet cola over top. Something must've reacted with the soda, because the whole glass exploded, sending pieces of glass all over the counter and into my hand.

"Ah! Ow!" I whined, more surprised the glass exploded, than the fact the glass pieces went into my hand.

Victor the murderer came running to my rescue.

"Are you all right? Oh, man, what were you doing?"

"Oh, I had to clean up something off the counter. Ow!"

"Here, you'd better clean that cut before it, like, gets infected."

"I can do it."

"But your hand is——"

"I can do it!"

You try and kill someone and suddenly they act all nice. Victor helped me bandage the cut, much to my embarrassment. I had to remember, this guy killed Viv. This guy killed Viv.

"Thanks, Victor."

"Sure."

I stopped him, suddenly getting an idea.

"Have you seen my balcony? It's really cool."

"Well, uh, I don't think I should go outside—"

I pulled Victor into my bedroom and out onto the balcony. The only thing out there was this gas grill Mark bought me for my birthday. Of course, *he* was the only one that ever used it.

"Hey, this *is* nice," said Victor, impressed.

For a second he threw me off kilter. What the fuck was he looking at?

"Whoa, you got trees and woods back here. And the sky's so big! I should move to New Jersey."

"That's nothing, look down there. Pine cones!"

"Where?"

Victor leaned way over the railing. I closed my eyes and pushed him.

"Whoa!" Thud.

A few seconds of silence and I breathed I sigh. Now to get rid of the body. Oh, God. I didn't think of that.

"I'm all right. I'm all right," he suddenly said. "I think I landed on somebody's garden."

"Don't move, I'll be right down."

What a pain in the ass. Maybe I can run him down with my car. Tch, no. I just bought that car. Oh! Why can't people just die when you kill them?!

"Mindy?"

Victor was stumbling around in the darkness behind the apartment complex. Most of my neighbors were either out for the evening or too old and deaf to hear anything. There's this nice old man that lives four doors down that chops wood for exercise. I spotted his rusty axe, picked it up and waited for Victor to turn the corner.

"Shhh, be quiet," I said to him. "You'll wake up the neighbors. I'm over here."

"Where?"

When Victor cleared the corner, I swung the axe back. It wasn't as heavy, when I got it into the air. Unfortunately, that was because the head popped off as soon as I swung back. It went through my windshield and set off the car alarm.

"Tch! Dammit!"

"What are you doing, Mindy?"

I hit Victor with the axe handle, knocking him unconscious. Fortunately, I had my keys handy and shut off the car alarm, before anyone woke up. I dragged Victor inside.

When he woke up, I had him tied up and in the bathtub. I filled it with cold water.

"Hey, what's goin' on?" he asked, half amused and half scared.

"I know you killed Viv."

I couldn't help it. I started to cry. Partly because Viv was dead and partly because of what Victor was making me do.

"Why? WHY?!"

"I didn't kill her, Mindy! I swear, I swear!"

"Look, I know this sounds weird but, Mark has this way of knowing things. It's never wrong, so I know you're a liar. Now, I got this old hair dryer and if you just shut up, you can go nice and peaceful."

I dropped the hairdryer into the water. Victor jumped, but appeared to still be breathing.

"I think you have to plug it in first."

"I don't need your help!" I snapped. "Don't tell me how to kill you! And don't be so fucking nice!"

"I'm sorry."

"Stop apologizing!"

I pulled the hairdryer out of the water.

"I'm sorry. You killed Viv, so you have to die."

"But—"

"Uh-uh. Just take it like a man."

Again, I was really not paying attention. I plugged the dryer in with it soaking wet. The lights in the whole apartment complex dimmed and I got thrown back against the wall. I must've blacked out for a few minutes, because the next thing I knew, Victor had just stepped over me and was running out of the apartment. I ran into the kitchen and got a knife, but as I ran for the door, it hit me.

I had this amazing epiphany. I remembered Victor in the alley. It hit me like an acid flashback. He went out the fire exit with these worn, brown Dockers. I remembered them, because I was with Viv when she bought them. But when Victor came out of the alley, he was wearing sneakers. I could see it with such an awful clarity, I knew right then, Victor wasn't the killer. I ran outside, hoping to catch him.

"Victor! Victor, wait! I made a mistake!"

"Stay away from me!"

Now, this is why it's all Mark's fault. After he called me and met up with his cop friend, Goda, they both got into their cars and rushed over here. Mark was trying to show off, so he was driving like a maniac. Poor Victor wasn't paying attention and Mark skidded into him. You see? Totally not my fault.

<u>CHAPTER 18</u> (Mark): Still Batting A Thousand

Why couldn't I have hit Mindy? Goda, who nearly slammed into me when I stopped, came running up. Always the cop, he kneeled next to Victor to assess his condition. I'll never hear the end of this.

"Victor? Victor! Oh, my God! You killed him!" shrieked Mindy across the parking lot.

"Me?!" I said incredulous, getting out to check him. "What are you doing with that kitchen knife?"

"Oh. I was, uh— I was having a pear."

"You hate pears."

"I gave them a second chance!"

"The ambulance is on its way, don't move, pal. Fix, where do you think you are? Daytona?"

"Tell him. Tell him!"

Mindy gave me the punch. The "he's-wrong-so-take-my-side" punch. I hate the punch.

"Gimme that." I felt taking the knife out of Mindy's hand was a wise move at this juncture. "If we could just all calm down here. We can go inside, have a freshly barbe-cued burger and wait for the ambulance. Oh, and by the way, he didn't kill Viv. And don't punch me."

She hit me again!

"What do you mean he didn't do it! You said! You said!" Mindy took me aside and whispered, "The Stuff."

"It must've been wrong."

"You said its never wrong!" she insisted, shouting in my ear and hitting me again. "You said! You said!"

"Don't hit me!"

"But you said!"

Our conversation is a blur after that. Mindy and I have argued so much over the years, we learned to tune ourselves out. The details of the actual problem take a backseat, logic goes on vacation and you're basically seeing how badly each one of us wants to win.

Take my advice, if you argue with a woman, just let the argument take its natural course and it's over that much sooner. I guess we must've gotten on Goda's nerves, because he was suddenly standing, all red-faced and furious.

"Shut the FUCK! UP!" he bellowed.

We fell dead silent, more because we had forgotten Goda was even there. Somewhere in a nearby apartment, a couple applauded Goda's sentiments.

"Both of ya sit on the goddamn curb until the ambulance gets here and don't say a fucking word!"

And we did. It was kind of like having your father yell at you on a trip. Just sit in the back, shut up and walk on eggs until he decides to loosen up.

In the Emergency Room of the hospital, Mindy told me what she had done, but I was only half paying attention. I was more anxious to compare notes with Goda and grill Victor. And hopefully, he wouldn't decide to sue me. As Goda came back from the vending machines with a coffee, the doctor walked in.

"How is he doc? He gonna make it?"

"Oh, certainly," replied the bemused doc. "Although, uh, he'll be in a little pain for a while. You can see him, if you like."

We started to follow the doctor, but he gestured to Mindy.

"Oh, okay," agreed Mindy, sitting back down.

Then Goda's beeper went off.

"Ah, shit," he muttered. "It's an emergency. Find out what he knows. If he gets cute, tell 'em about our little Japanese friends."

Goda rushed off to a payphone. I had my instructions.

"Fix, man, Fix," Victor mumbled happily.

He was surprisingly happy to see me, considering I just ran him over.

"Hey, I think Mindy tried to kill me."

"Nah," I assured him. "She was just kidding around. Trust me, I know when she has murder in her eyes."

"That cop was asking me questions. Should I get a lawyer or something?" asked Victor, completely ignorant of our country's laws and Seventies' TV police dramas. "Mark, you can be my lawyer, right?"

"Okay. Then as your attorney I advise you to answer Goda's questions."

"Okay."

"Let me start you off. We're at the Alien Blue. You, Mindy and Viv exit, Mindy comes back and drinks me a hundred dollars poorer. Where did you and Viv go?"

"I don't know."

"Victor," I said threateningly. "I'm gonna call Mindy in here."

"Well, I— I mean, uhhhh..."

I could hear the wheels squeaking in Victor's head. God, I wish I had a nickel for every second I lost waiting for pea-brains like him to catch up. You want to know the value of a good education? Five minutes, man. Five *fucking* minutes. That's about all the time I can stand waiting for the dullard at the video store to ring up my video or the genius at Castle Burger to get my fries to the window. Without the stress of the Stupid, I think we'd all be in much better health.

"Victor!" I growling, gritting my teeth at him.

"I was in the alley," he finally remembered. "Yeah, I was making a deal with some guy. Viv and Mindy were at the fire escape, ya know, doing their lesbian thing."

"I missed lesbianism?" I inquired, momentarily distracted.

"No, not really. They just did a little more hugging and kissing than normal."

"Victor, I've just about had it. Now either tell me a good lesbian story or get to the point!"

"That's it, man! I dealt the rest of my coke— What was left of it, to this guy. Then, I don't know, I must've passed out. Viv and Mindy were gone, I went to some dive on the waterfront and passed out in a dumpster. Next thing ya know, everybody's trying to kill me."

"So you didn't see anything?! C'mon, Victor. Viv is dead! And according to Mindy and a reliable source, she got into a cab with a guy who looked exactly like you!"

"I didn't get in no cab, Mark. I swear! I didn't have any money!"

"What about the coke you sold?"

"I didn't pay for the drugs yet, I couldn't afford a cab, man! And Viv don't go with me no more! You think she'd take me home? No way. Not in years. I'm just her dealer, now."

Victor was scaring me. He made sense and I believed him.

"Wait, what happened to the guy you dealt the coke to?"

"Him? Um, I guess he left."

"What did he look like?"

"Real familiar, now that you mention it."

"C'mon, Victor, if you know him, just say—"

"No, not like that. Like he was famous. That guy who does the commercial. With the stuff."

Well, that narrows it down.

"Who? What stuff?"

"Umm, it's in a bottle..."

"Shampoo? Beer? Mustard?"

"Mustard's not in a bottle."

"Just think!"

"I think he used to be in a shampoo commercial, but that's not the one I'm thinking of. This was like a medicine, like a pain killer."

"Aspirin? Antacid?"

"Hemorrhoid stuff!"

"Hemorrhoid creme's not in a bottle you putz!"

"That's it, though. He did the Hemorrhoid commercial. I think he was a football player."

"That's Nate Jordan, the ex-quarterback! Are you telling me you sold coke to the *Brooklyn Bomber*, then he took Viv home and killed her?! Did he give you a free twelve ounce sample too?!"

"Well, he *looked* like him. Hey, that cop doesn't know about the drugs, right?"

"Victor, we just left Viv's apartment thirty minutes ago. There were about a dozen, very angry Japanese martial arts students there looking to cut you to little pieces. So either you start making some sense or we're going to let them visit with you."

I had enough of Victor's nonsense and stormed out of the room. He shouted for me until I got out of earshot. Goda was back in the waiting room with Mindy.

"So?"

"He didn't see anything. Some guy he sold drugs to— Looked like Nate Jordan, I don't know. I think we're back to square one."

Goda kicked over the magazine table in frustration. I looked at Mindy bewildered.

"Chill out, man. He might remember something. In the meantime, you can fill me in on the other victims."

"I can't, that's what the call was about!"

"What?" I looked at Mindy. She's no help.

"They stole his files," she whispered to me.

"Those feds, I told ya about. My captain called the bureau to see if we could get a look at one of the files. No one knew what the fuck he was talking about!"

Oh, no. Not him.

"What were their names?" I asked Goda, my heart pounding.

"What difference does it—"

"What were their names?!" I insisted.

"Agent, uh, Keystone and Nash— No, Mass. What? You know 'em?"

"Keystone, Pennsylvania. Mass, Massachusetts," repeated Mindy, putting it together aloud.

"Those guys weren't feds. They were two of the Colonials."

"Who?"

I grabbed Mindy by the arm, suddenly having the urge to go back to the office and find my bigger gun. Goda had other ideas.

"Who?" he said, turning me around.

"Look," I said looking around for the hidden cameras and microphones. "You know I have friends on the Liberators, right?"

"These Colonials are some kind of superheroes?"

"No, their boss," added Mindy.

"The Colonials are just his henchmen. Ex-CIA guys, Green Berets, Black Ops— All that bullshit. There are always thirteen Colonials and they always take the codenames of the first thirteen states. That's his trademark."

"Who's trademark?" Goda said impatiently.

I knew he wasn't going to believe me, but I said it anyway.

"Patriot 13."

"Patriot 13?"

"You heard of 'em?"

"Yeah, and I heard of the Easter Bunny. Patriot 13's just something they tell the tourists over at Independence Hall."

"I'm telling you, I've seen him!" I insisted, trying not to lose my temper.

"He kidnapped us and tried to kill us," added Mindy, backing me up.

"Patriot 13's supposed to be some kind of legend, like Paul Bunyon or Uncle Sam. He supposed to be a good guy, right?"

"Look, you know how there's the police, but then there's the undercover guys and then there's the FBI, but then there's the CIA? Well, you got your basic superheroes, the Liberators and then you got the super-psycho spies, like Patriot 13. I'm telling you Goda, half the Liberators shit a brick if you just mention his name."

"So why would he steal my files? Who's he covering for?"

"Who does the CIA cover for? Anything to protect national interests. He's a fanatic, Goda. A powerful fanatic who hates me and scares the shit out of me."

"Mark, can you take me home?"

This was all too much for Mindy. She bit her bottom lip and tried to hold back the tears. I think she just did it so Goda would leave me alone and we could leave. It's amazing how we band together when someone causes us mutual discomfort. Goda followed us outside the Emergency Room entrance.

"I'm not finished with you," insisted Goda.

"Goda, we're out of it. Good luck."

"No, I don't think so. Not if you want to keep your secret, secret."

Mindy and I stopped.

"He knows?" she whispered to me.

I nodded, then turned back to Goda.

"Goda, you don't have any idea of what you're dealing with. The Patriot had my P.I. license revoked, had me audited, wiped out my bank accounts, changed my Social Security Card number! And that was just for starters!"

"Yeah, well he pissed me off!" said Goda, as if that were reason enough for me to change my mind. "Now are ya in or not?"

"Fine," I said reluctantly. "But don't come crying to me when you find out you're legally dead. You gonna question Victor?"

"No, first I gotta go home and write down everything I can remember about the other victims."

"Wait a minute! I just remembered! Aldo was supposed to fax me the same information!"

"Who's Aldo?"

"I don't know, but that doesn't matter. Meet me at my office tomorrow morning at eleven."

Mindy and I climbed into the Fix Mobile.

"Eleven? Why so late?"

"We like to sleep in," added Mindy.

CHAPTER 19 (Narrator): Grey Skies for the Weather Man

Winston Williamson (yes, that was his real name), was from the old school of crimefighting. One of the last not to retire, quit, or die, despite the new reign of Liberators leaders. The general public knew him better as The Weather Man, named for his penchant for forecasting crimes, as well as weather patterns, which aided him in his righteous fight against evil.

These days, however, the line between black and white was mired in grey skies. Cases of patricide, incest, and acts too unspeakable to mention, had made Winston, for the first time in twenty years, think about hanging up his mask. Corruption amongst the Liberators, during last year's scandal, had hit him hard. Winston felt he couldn't trust his own teammates.

His Liberator status was Class S, which stood for "Solo", which meant he was allowed to work alone, despite his lack of superhuman abilities. He didn't even have to wear the standard Liberator uniform, which he felt was ridiculous, except for official functions and photo ops. Winston was working Fairmont Park, donned in a skin tight, black outfit with patterns of black clouds and lightning bolts. He used to just carry his nunchukos and a utility belt filled with an array of his homemade specialty weapons. These days, all he was permitted to carry were government-approved, non-lethal restraints, like mace, and a policeman's service revolver. Although, he still carried the nunchukos, despite warnings that he and the Liberators could be sued if he used them.

Fairmont Park was dangerous at night, but with Winston's light-intensifying goggles and the predicted full moon, he was able to see everything clearly. Two Japanese youths had cornered a third by the Centennial memorial. They were in such a hurry, they had left the doors to their Calvary mini-van open, which made a steady ping, ping, ping, in the otherwise silent park.

The third youth appeared to be sick or hurt, crouched in a fetal position, while one of the boys poured gasoline on him. The other stood over him with a small sword, poking him into submission every so often. This was more than Winston could take. Evil had to be punished! Regulations be damned!

"Gentlemen!" he announced, leaping out of the darkness with his nunchuckos. "I am the Weather Man and you should snow better."

The youth with the gasoline, reeled from one of his strikes. The second seemed hesitant to leave his quarry unguarded, despite the awful pun. He swung at Winston, who ducked and announce, "High Front!", then swung again, causing Winston to jump and announce, "Low Front!" Winston finished the encounter with a few well-placed nunchucko hits. The boys fell to the ground.

"With a hundred percent chance of you two going to jail."

The two youths, abandoning their antics, ran in opposite directions into the darkness of Fairmont. Winston smirked, he'd find them later, but first, the victim. He turned to help Takashi to his feet.

"Don't be alarmed, citizen. I'm a licensed law enforcement agent of the City of Philadelphia. Sir? Can you hear me?"

As Winston bent down closer, he turned Takashi's gasoline-soaked face toward him. Strange, cloudy goo was pouring out of his eyes and mouth. It was the last thing Winston saw, before he himself became engulfed in goo.

"Oh, my G——"

CHAPTER 20 (Narrator): Night of a Thousand Faces

Fix and Mindy spent the night on the fold-out cot at Inevitable Investigations. Mindy curled up in a ball on one side, while Mark whispered reassurances in the dark.

At the Goda household, Tommy had the nightmare again. He stood at the edge of a river of blood, while Carl Cannon stood above him, laughing from a mountain of skulls. Tina Goda woke him up because the phone rang. It was the morgue.

"*You're* gonna be dead if this isn't important," threatened Goda.

"Sorry, Lieutenant, I thought you should know immediately," explained Espanoza.

"Know what?"

"Your Jamaicans are both dead. Shipped down here about an hour ago. But one of them disappeared."

"You sure he was dead then?"

"I'd assume the hospital checked closely, but..."

Espanoza examined the body drawer again. It had been broken open from the inside. A thin film of semi-transparent goo collected in a puddle in the center of the drawer.

"I suppose if he acquired the right drugs, he could fake it, but.... It's all very strange, I thought you should know."

"Yeah, yeah, thanks," replied Goda hanging up.

Goda slipped quickly back to sleep and dreamt he was in a limo with a grossly incompetent driver with glowing green eyes.

At the hospital, the night nurse, overworked and underpaid, dosed off at her post while reading a magazine. The blinking light from Room 341, Victor's room, continued to flash steadily.

Victor's roommate, a blundering amateur skier, who'd ended up with two broken legs, one broken arm and in traction, was awakened by moaning in the bed nearby. The light from outside the hallway backlit Victor's curtain, which had been pulled around him by the nurse. Victor was sitting up in bed moaning in pain. The skier steadily pushed the nurse button with his unbroken thumb. He watched in helpless horror as Victor's chest burst open and gooy contents spilled out, then smothered and consumed him.

At the same time, Sven, the Son of Thor, left this evening's sleeping companion to sleep in his bed alone. The Asgardian feared he might roll over the thin, supermodel in the middle of the night, crushing her with his mighty bulk. He spent the night carving runes into his favorite end table.

The Wolf growled to himself, as the waning moon was enshrouded by a sky of clouds. He took no comfort in having the warmest cell on the block. He just kept murmuring "Seventy-five years," like a bitter mantra in his sleep.

Somewhere in New York, Mark's friend Smitty curled up to sleep with a half empty vodka bottle inside an abandoned Roy Boy's. He stared up in a drunken stupor, trying to touch one particular star in the sky just beyond the partially boarded up drive thru window. He looked at it longingly, then passed out for the night.

But not everyone slept.

Below the blue lights that spanned the Ben Franklin Bridge, in the shadow of the abandoned piers near the waterfront, deep beneath the bowels of an abandoned Franklin stove factory, he watched.

The only dim illumination in this rat-infested, dry-rotted building were his monitors. He sat in his web of computer equipment. All state of the art and all compact enough that he could carry it on his person. He could reach out to almost any part of the world. The cellphone, the modem and the satellites did the rest. All you needed were the right codes and the will to use them.

One keystroke and he could find you. Two keystrokes and he could get you. Three keystrokes and he could ruin you. Four keystrokes and— Well, only one person ever got past three.

It occurred to him how often he'd returned to Philadelphia, where it all started. His career with the Liberators, back when they trafficked in spandex tights and hope, rather than public relations and empty promises. Back when America stood for something other than the twisted ideals of an idolized few.

His friends, his family— A faded memory. Nothing but the work now. His dedication getting him through the darkness and the loneliness. The dedication of a man to the greatest country on Earth and the burden of a legend, known as Patriot 13.

"Sir," said Agent Garden.

This was a request for permission to approach. Sometimes the Patriot's screen held classified info. Sometimes it was a "need-to-know" and sometimes it was a "never-know". The Patriot dimmed the appropriate monitor and gestured for Garden to approach. He crossed the room in the prearranged pattern.

Garden could barely make him out in the darkness. The Patriot's dark blue, skin tight face mask was ringed with thirteen stars. His suit was a drab, soulless gray. His body was long and lanky. Too big for the folding chair he was sitting on, so his arms and legs hung about him, like a titan sitting on a mountain. And even sitting down, Garden felt the Patriot's presence looking down upon him.

"Operation: One Leg was a success, sir," reported Keystone. "All documents and evidence pertaining to the Flayer have been destroyed. Agents Mass and Keystone retrieved the information without incident."

"Not quite," corrected the Patriot.

"Sir?"

"There was an unauthorized fax from the Philadelphia Police department twelve minutes before Mass and Keystone arrived. Information pertaining to the case was sent to Inevitable Investigations in Pennsauken, New Jersey."

Garden was one of the Patriot's hand-picked, top of his class, special forces. He had an IQ of 167 and a reaction time that seemed almost inhuman. Yet, he was flustered.

"Sir, I— I'll send a team immediately."

"No," insisted 13. "I know this individual."

The Patriot accessed a file and pulled up a picture of Mark. In the picture, he was eating a cheesesteak and dripping ketchup on his shirt.

"He's a private investigator, Mark Mammon. Calls himself Fix. No doubt he's working on the murder investigation."

"I can have him eliminated, sir. I'll see to it myself, personally."

"Garden," began the Patriot, his voice betraying annoyance. "If I thought you had any chance of doing it, I would've sent you months ago."

"I don't understand, sir. Who is this Fix?"

"Are you familiar with our paranormal ratings system?"

"Yes, sir."

"I rate a Class 8 norm, quite high for a human. Fix's associate, Sven or Jonny Plazzz, as he is known, rates as a Class 13 Arcana Entity. The most powerful Liberator, when he was alive, rated as a Class 18 Technological Entity. Would you like to know how we rated Fix?"

"Yes, sir."

"Class 53, Unknown Entity. And that's just based on what we know."

"My God, sir. Doesn't that make him a threat to national security just by the very nature of his power?"

"It would, but he isn't aware of just how powerful he is and that's both his strength and his weakness. No, we'll leave Fix alone for now. He's a project. *My* personal project. Understood?"

"But sir, the investigation would—"

"That is the fault of our—" The Patriot paused, remembering a time when he didn't refer to serial killers in such politically correct terms. "Our indiscreet associate. Contact him. Tell him to move his base of operations, but let him know we expect the research to be delivered on time."

"Yes, sir. Right away."

Garden began to leave.

"Oh, and remember," added the Patriot. "Keep your distance during the meeting. Your predecessor didn't and— Well, he is, afterall, indiscreet."

<u>CHAPTER 21</u> (Mark): The Alien loved his Beer

Goda was pissed by the time we got back to my office. Mindy and I had to run home to shower and change. Then I got caught up in some phone calls which had nothing to do with the case or Goda or me, for that matter. Then I had to mow the lawn. (My parents don't charge me rent, I have to do something.) Another shower and another phone call. Anyway, by the time we stopped for cheesesteaks and got back to the office it was about 2:30. Goda was pissed.

But, hey, I bought him a cheesesteak.

"I'd like to wrap this case some time this century!" he growled.

We found him talking to Toby, the really annoying guy who manages the Tally-Ho for Mr. Allenscott, my landlord. Toby's just a little smarter than the Rainman.

"And what's the deal with that guy?" Goda gestured toward Toby. "He retarded or what?"

"Or what," Mindy and I answer simultaneously.

"The cheesesteak's good, huh?" I asked, trying to divert his attention.

"I don't care, you want to work with me, you don't start this late....and, yeah, it's good."

"Mr. Submarine's makes the best. It's this little place over in—"

"Mark, I don't think he really cares," added Mindy. "So what's our next move?"

"Mindy, shouldn't you be at work?" I asked, slightly annoyed, walking back into the office.

"Becky'll punch me in. We can swing by this afternoon, I'll make an appearance, steal some office supplies——"

"Ooo, I need envelopes," I remind her.

"The big kind or the regular?"

"Can you get both? I like to have a selection."

"Ex*cuse* me!" Goda pipes up with a mouthful of cheese and meat. "Where's your fax?"

"Over there," I gesture to my office.

While Mindy and I finish lunch, we listen to Goda try to find the fax in my mess of an office.

"It's near the window," Mindy instructs.

"Jesus Christ, Fix. Is this how you run an office?"

"Hey, do you know how many times I've been broken into? I might as well stop locking the door," I counter. "At least this way it'll take some time for them to find something important."

"Is there where you keep the green stuff?"

"None of your business. You find the fax?"

"Yeah, it looks like its all here. You gotta give me the number of this Aldo. He must work in my department."

"I don't think he'd talk to you. He's like an enigma. He started calling me with jobs and clues a few years ago. You want to help me find him?"

"Why don't you just use your magic snot?"

"It's not snot! Well, I don't think its snot. Anyway, that wouldn't be fair. It's kind of a challenge."

"Maybe later. You wanna hear about the other victims or what?"

I nodded.

"Your friend was a twenty-seven-year-old, white female, interior decorator. My last victim was a thirty-four-year-old, Latino male, bridge construction worker. The other four victims were an eighty-two-year-old, Afro-American housewife, a fifteen-year-old oriental male student, a sixty-four-year-old, retired, white male security guard and a twenty-two-year-old, Indian male college student. All different locations, all different times of death. The only thing that's consistent is that the victims were cut open and their livers were stolen."

"So who do you think did it?" asks Mindy.

"Most serial killers fit a standard profile. All their lives, they've been powerless, the killing is their way of gaining control."

"Yeah, but wouldn't the anger be directed at a particular type of person. Someone the killer associates his anger with?" I asked.

"That's what so weird about this case. He's all over. It's not about women or men or race or religion. That's why I thought it could've been Carl."

"Who did he kill?"

"Police officers, teachers— People in a position of authority— Basically, anybody that got in his way. Mindy, can you think of anyone that Viv might have known who coulda done this?"

"She dated a lot of guys, but they were usually all professional types."

"Jack the Ripper was a doctor," I added. "But why take the liver? What is it with livers? Maybe he's one of those donor killers. Sells the liver on the black market."

"Yeah, but why leave the rest of it? Besides, the way the liver was ripped out— They can't use that."

While the three of us wracked our brains I looked over the photos of the crime scenes. I recognized a pattern in the blood of one of the crime scenes. Now where did I see that?

"Hey, did you run the cassette through the fingerprint guys?" I asked.

"Yeah, nuthin'."

Then, it suddenly hit me.

"My old boom box."

"What?"

"My old boom box, that what makes this pattern in the blood."

"Why would the killer carry a radio all the way up the bridge?"

"Maybe it was a boring murder."

"My head hurts," added Mindy.

I busted out my favorite detective tool. The dictionary.

"I know. Let's see," I mumbled to myself. "Livers..."

"Expecting to find his picture under murderers? If you want to find out about livers, you gotta talk to professionals."

"Dictionaries are written by professionals," I countered. "You mean to tell me, in your entire career, you never used a dictionary during a case? What do your reports look like?"

"I got spell check!"

While Goda and I argued over the finer points of forensics and Webster's, Mindy rolled her eyes and decided to get a soda from the Tally-Ho vending machine. But, no sooner had she opened the door, than she let out a blood-curdling scream of terror. I nearly fell backwards in my chair. Goda drew his gun and kept shouting at Mindy to move out of his line of fire.

But Mindy has this sustained, cinema scream. She was screaming so loud, I don't think she could hear Goda. I scrambled to my feet and tried to use the sleeve holster. You know, the bit from the movie "Taxi Driver", where DeNiro is standing at the mirror and the gun shoots into his hand. I got one for each sleeve of my overcoat, but I haven't quite gotten the bugs out of it. The gun overshot my palm by a few inches, graced my fingertips and did a dance over the edge of the desk as I fumbled for it.

Then, I looked up.

A hideous green-gray mass, covered in slimy dripping eyeballs and mouths with little teeth oozed its way into the doorway. Sure, in a movie, you'd laugh at it. But when you see it, hear it and smell it close up, you get this sharp pang of terror, as if someone just walked into the room and explained to you that the reality you know is all a sham. "Whoosh!" goes the rug, right out from under you.

Goda cautiously made his way to Mindy, pulling her out of harm's way and fully ready to fight his way out the back. Fortunately, before it could go any farther, I realized who it was.

"Smitty! You dick!" I greeted. "Where the Hell have you *been*, man?!"

With a flourish, the monster congealed, sprouted a two-thousand-dollar business suit and morphed into Smitty's street personae, John Schmidt. He kind of resembled this burned-out college student, with salt and pepper hair and sunken eyes.

"Hey, Fatboy!" greeted Smitty. "Got beer?"

"You asshole!" squealed Mindy. "I nearly had a heart attack!"

"What?" he said innocently. "What? C'mon, lighten up. That was funny."

Except for calling me "Fatboy", I agreed, but I suppressed a laugh.

"I'm a cop, jack-off," added Goda, half-angry and half embarrassed. "I don't care what you are, you do that again and you'll be spendin' the rest of the week in county lock-up for disturbin' the peace!"

Goda grabbed the rest of his sandwich and stormed out of the room. Mindy took my car keys and followed.

"Wait, where—"

"I gotta go get my windshield fixed," Mindy said quickly.

"I'll be back at the station getting a psych profile. You want to work this case, Fix, be there in a half hour," threatened Goda as he exited.

The door slammed. I frowned at Smitty.

"So, uh, you got that beer?"

I rolled my eyes and searched my mini-fridge for a bottle. I came up with one last Greener's Brew, left over from my birthday party last spring. Smitty chugged the whole thing and tossed the empty in the vicinity of my trash can.

"Ah!" he exhaled satisfactorily. "That's my boy! What's in the CD changer?"

Smitty brushed by me and powered up my Fidelic stereo. I had been in sort of a pretentious mood, so the *Achtung Baby* CD was in the carousel. Smitty mumbled along to "Mysterious Ways" and rubbed his ass against a speaker in a purposely pathetic Bono impression.

"You really know how to clear a room, *Drunk Boy*," I added. "Got any more parades to rain on today?"

"What's with the cop?"

"Forget him. What happened to you the other night?"

"Ah, I had to go to Austin," Smitty explained, annoyed by the very mention of it.

He picked up some of the papers on my desk and flipped idly through. The man has the attention span of a fruit fly.

"It would be nice if you showed up *once*, when people expected you. Sven's pissed."

"Oh, right, like you would've done anything different if I was there."

"That's not the point. You stood up your date. I got in trouble with Mindy—"

"Oooo!" he mocked. "Not Mindy! God forbid I upset the Great Rag Queen! Ooooo! Fuck her, let's go to the casino."

"I can't, I'm busy and don't talk that way about Mindy."

"C'mon, I'm doing a show. I got a suite," he tempted.

"Mindy's best friend was killed—I'm in the middle of this case—"

"Fine, forget it."

Smitty's tone suddenly turned ugly. His impish charm quickly collapsed into bold, selfishness. It was his move. Smitty had this way of putting you on the defensive and making you feel guilty, even though he was usually the one at fault. I guess he was feeling lonely and irritable, but I didn't have time for his nonsense. Not today.

"You come in here, act like a dick and then try to make *me* feel guilty about it?"

"No, it's okay," the wounded Smitty replied. "I'm-sure-you're-*very*-busy-bye."

And with that, Smitty strolled out of the office. He probably expected me to follow and, on most days, I probably would have. He was kind of like the older cousin I never had, always goading me into skydiving or drag racing or some insane activity, then leaving me in the lurch at the last minute. Angry and red-faced, I'd find him in some bar later, stoked to the gills. The next thing you know, we'd be laughing and telling the story, as if we were conquering heroes.

I guess everybody has a friend like that, who simultaneously brings out the best and worst in you. Who compliments you on all your strengths, while exploiting all your weaknesses. Tells you a joke at your expense, than asks you to laugh. That was Smitty. The happy drunk. Party animal. A frat of one.

"See you on Tuesday," I called after him.

Tuesday was poker night. Now that I knew he was on the East coast, he'd have to show for that. Considering the "I'm- so-desperate-for-attention" attitude, he'd probably come just to make sure I didn't find another poker player to replace him on Tuesdays.

My poker group would never do that. Despite his sporadic attendance, Smitty's rich and the cards hate him.

I gathered up a few notes (my dictionary, of course), locked the office and headed for the train station. (Thanks a lot for stranding me here, Min'.) Just as I rounded the corner, I spot Smitty's limo down the street in front of the liquor store. Parked just down the road, a squat little detective with one leg.

"Hello!" I beamed, slipping into the back seat and slamming the door.

Goda jumped and pulled out his gun.

"Man, you are trigger happy," I added. "What are you doing here?"

"Get out of the car, Fix. I'm tailing a potential suspect."

Smitty walked out of the front door of the liquor store with a case of Red King, the beer that's practically brewed skunked. Even with all his money, Smitty always drank cheap.

"Oh, you gotta be kidding. It was a joke!"

"Hey, in case you haven't noticed, you're friend ain't exactly human!"

"Yeah, so are half the Liberators. So's the guy guarding the president. You aren't, if you want to get technical."

"He's a super that can change his shape. If he could do all that, why couldn't he turn his hands into knives?"

"Oh, c'mon."

"Well, could he do it?"

"Yeah, but—"

"He knows you, he knows your girlfriend. Did he know the victim?"

"Yeah."

"Was he at the club?"

"No!" I pointed out, but then added meekly. "But he was supposed to be there..."

"So, Smitty runs into the victim outside the club, they go back to her place, she says no and he make sushi out of her. Case closed."

"Oh, right, that works. What about the pile of bodies, genius? Why'd he kill them?"

"I don't know, but he's the best lead I got."

"I ain't getting out of the car."

"Fine, come along. But don't get cute with me. You try and cover for your buddy—Oh, ho!"

Goda was trying to scare me, but I wasn't buying it this time. The tough cop act was wearing thin. I think he was just desperate. Smitty opened the door to his limo. Inside, his stereo was blaring the soundtrack to "Live and Let Die" so loud, his chauffeur took to wearing airport headphones to protect his ears. After a few minutes, Smitty's limo finally pulled out of the lot. Several empty beer cans bounced their way out of the back door as it took off heading south.

"So," began Goda. "How'd you meet Smitty?"

CHAPTER 22 (Mark): The Alien and Huey Lewis

As soon as he asks the question, I am immediately taken back to my salad days of 1987. (Not for real, just metaphorically.) I was twenty-one and enrolled in Camden District Community College. Or, as the locals know it, the thirteenth grade. My course curriculum read like a rap sheet for a guy who didn't know what the hell he wanted to do with his life. I was taking a combination of Archaeology, Law Enforcement, Fencing, Photography and Science Fiction writing, which, had I stayed enrolled, would've probably qualified me to be Indiana Jones.

Campus life wasn't much, since there was no place to live on campus. (I, of course, commuted via my new, used Nippon.) The out of town students all had to get apartments in a nearby complex, which was half student housing and half locals who used to be students. Most peoples' attendance was so tenuous, you got the feeling that college was an excuse to run around naked, drink yourself blind and puke in a stranger's apartment. Everyone missed classes, no one missed a party.

It was at one of these very parties I met Smitty. I dropped out of CDC, but he didn't even come close to graduating. Mainly because the only thing Smitty made time for was arm bending.

A group of students had formed their own unofficial frat called "The Second Floor Brothers". Their charter was probably something like "Drink, drink, and drink some more". The complex had apartments on the first and second floor and all the brothers had second floor living accommodations, much to the displeasure of anyone who lived below who liked to go to bed early.

Normally, I don't join such things. I find the group mentality of any organization to be uncomfortable. But, Mindy had just moved away to Virginia to live at her college and our long distance romance was falling apart. It was the first time we broke up, not long after our infamous Delaware trip, and I was feeling very alone. And Hell, this was the heady late eighties', when VH was still cool, and gorging yourself on sex, drugs and money was becoming a way a life.

I drifted down a hallway of open doors, while *Hip to be Square* shook the windows and the SF Brothers tossed beer bottles at random passersby. Two of the brothers had emptied a fire extinguisher in the hall, then decided that wasn't enough and were trying to pull the *case* for the fire extinguisher off the wall. Lonny, then the Resident Advisor stepped in to stop them. After whining, "Hey, fellas, c'mon," the brothers de-pantsed him and took off. In another room, I spotted a group of three brothers cheering a fourth as he had sex with a girl that probably had to get her mother to drive her here.

"Hey, Brother Mark!"

Leon was from my Music Appreciation class and was destined to become the front man for Neon Loser, the most aptly named garage band on the planet. But back then, he had rock star looks and an Italian sports car. Leon was one of those guys who could talk almost any woman he wanted into bed. I mean, *fast*. Not even a date. He'd just walk into a bar and boom, he'd be slammin' her an hour later and listening to her moan about how she'd "never done this before."

"Uh, hi, Brother Leon," I mumbled. "Where's the beer?"

"Two doors up, on the left, in the bathroom, in the toilet full of ice," he instructed, rocking back and forth. He gestured to the girl. "You want seconds?"

"You're cute, Leon, but you're not my type," I quipped sullenly.

The other brothers laughed, as I walked away. Leon was kinda a homophobe, so the comment pissed him off. I didn't care. I wanted to get into a fight. Anything to get some release that wouldn't put me up on Statutory Rape charges. Finally, I found the room with the keg.

It was quiet enough where I could sit and brood. My mood was dark and ugly. I don't normally drink, but I decided then to down a few beers and beat the crap out of the first brother to piss me off. A pile of cups were sitting in a filthy puddle near the base of the toilet, so I opted for a bathroom paper cup and pumped myself a Red King.

"Mindy," I muttered to myself, gulping it down.

"At that rate, you might as well suck it outta the tap."

The voice came from behind the shower curtain. A glassy-eyed Smitty pushed it aside. He was sitting in a bathtub full of beer, smoking a cigar.

"I'm sorry," I said, starting to leave.

"Nah, it's okay, stay. I'll cheer you up."

I rolled my eyes. He was only mildly irritating and in no condition for a fist fight. I pumped another beer.

"Look at this."

He turned on the tap. Golden liquid came out of the faucet.

"Hot and cold running beer!" he smiled. "Isn't that great?"

"How'd they do that?" I asked, astonished and impressed.

"We switched the hot water heater with a keg. And the landlord said it would explode! Ha!"

"Mark Mammon," I said shaking his hand.

"Call me, Smitty," he instructed. "Everybody does. Who's Mindy?"

"You don't want to go there."

"I'm a philosophy major," he said as if that were explanation enough. Weird thing was, I later found out Smitty aced every philosophy exam he ever took, all without cracking a text book.

"My girlfriend," I said, exhaling. "Actually my future *ex*-girlfriend— Long story."

"Women suck," he added earnestly, immediately sympathizing. "Women... Women *suck*."

Although he seemed unable to articulate his thoughts, I could tell Smitty was speaking from experience. He gestured in frustration, then looked to me for a reaction. The beer, however, was dissolving my resolve. I was quietly calculating how long it would take me to get to Virginia and how many classes I'd have to miss to make the trip.

"You live in this section?"

"Nah, I'm a local," I explained.

"Still living with your folks?" he asked, embarrassed for me.

"Just until I graduate," I said, annoyed. "What are you here to study? New ways to damage your liver?"

"Why are you so hostile?"

"My girlfriend and I— We—," I stammered, exasperated. "I don't know, it seemed we finally just got together, ya know. Things were just starting to click and then she moves to fucking *Virginia*!"

"Long drive for a blow job."

"*That* is *so rude*," I said, all at once disgusted and impressed by verbal bravado. "And it *is* a long drive."

"Women are like bathroom cups. There's always plenty of them and they're always in the bathroom."

There was an awkward silence. I refused to laugh at that one.

"I should go," I said suddenly, getting up to leave. "Bye, Drunk Boy."

"Wait," he said suspiciously. "You're going to go to Virginia, aren't you? You're going to go beg and grovel. Ewww, Mindy, please take me back!"

"Hey, I didn't come in here to be *mocked*, asshole!"

I bounced a cup off his head and stormed out of the bathroom. A few seconds later, Smitty caught up to me and turned me around. I was so ready to punch him, but when I turned around, he was fully clothed and bone dry. This lead me to believe the beer was laced with something other than barley and hops, so I put my travel plans on hold.

"C'mon, it was a joke," he assured. "Loosen up. It's a party!"

"I don't drink, Brother Smitty. At least, not in any amount that would be fun. I can't see much point in sitting around to watch everyone else lose their lunch."

"You're gonna stay sober, huh?" he asked to make sure. "You play poker?"

In the coming weeks, I'd win as much as three-hundred-dollars a week playing poker with the drunken brothers of SF. The sudden influx of money almost made me forget about Mindy. Smitty, of course, rarely showed up at the poker games. But, what worried me now, was that I had seen him at his most debauched. And he had a real bad opinion of not just Mindy, but women in general. All this, I kept from Goda, of course, but it made me wonder that split second. Could he?

<u>CHAPTER 23</u> (Goda): The Alien & the Palimony

This Fix was a piece of work. I'd seen a few of the Liberators. Even had lunch with their police liaison once, but Christ— At least she looked human. And even when you see the weird lookin' ones, you don't really think of them as aliens or gods or mutants or nothin'. They just look like they're dressed up for a movie.

But, shit, when one of them levitates in front of ya, when one of them looks at a stop sign and turns it to ice or when one of them picks up a bus—— Shit! It's like your whole friggin' perception goes out of whack! You're seein' it and starin' at it with your mouth dropped open. And you think, God! I am a little nuthin' compared to these guys! A friggin' bug!

But Fix, just shrugs his shoulders. "Oh, hey, by the way, meet my friend the alien abomination from another planet." And I thought I was desensitized.

"We met in college, but we didn't really become friends until I helped him with his divorce settlement."

"That thing was married?"

"Oh, yeah. She was— What the Hell was the porno she was in?"

"Forget that. What *is* he?"

"Long story."

"I'm gettin' tired of you sayin' that."

"Okay, okay," Fix relented.

He sort of exhaled in frustration, tryin' to think of a good way to explain it to me.

"This is gonna sound weird—"

"I'm past weird, tell."

"Okay. Smitty's a Kaltherian. An alien and— Keep this between us, right?"

"Yeah, whatever."

"Keep in mind, he told me this at a strip bar when he was *really* drunk, okay? Kaltherians are like amoebas. They're a highly complex, one-celled organism. Consequently, they evolved so they could change shape, color, texture— whatever. You followin' me?"

"Yeah, I got it."

"This is where it gets weird."

Is he kiddin' me?

"About fifty years ago, the Kaltherians made a pact with a group of other alien races, to rape and pillage primitive planets. Kind of like an evil version of Star Trek. They called themselves— and this part, I think Smitty made up— the Imperial Conquistadors."

"Why would—"

"The name doesn't matter, they were on a mission to explore new worlds, seek out new life and rob it blind. They reach Earth, right? We don't stand a chance, but the Conquistadors are all soldiers and they're not that bright. You with me?"

"I'm a trekkie," I growled, trying not to lose it. *"I'm wit you."*

"Smitty, had sorta been drafted into the Kaltherian Infantry. Their job was to work the battleroids. They're kind of like hollow robots. When the Kaltherian ships arrived at Earth, Smitty was depressed, so he went inside the battleroid early to sulk."

"What was he depressed about?"

"He never explained that. So, as the ships are getting ready to land, they start monitoring the broadcasts on Earth. Unfortunately, they just happen to start landing during the Orson Welles broadcast of H.G. Wells' *War of the Worlds*."

I just turn and look at him. Up to that point, I would've almost believed this.

"I know, I know, but the Conquistadors mistake the broadcast for the real thing. They think they're getting their asses kicked and abort the invasion. I told you, they weren't that smart. They end up stranding a few handful of aliens in their rush to leave."

"How many of the Liberators were part of the invasion?"

"Yeah, I thought of that too, but Smitty never met anyone outside his ship, so—"

"So he just got left behind."

"Well, there's more to it than that. The Kaltherian ship never even got to land. Something went wrong with their guidance system and it crashed in New Mexico. The whole crew was killed, except Smitty, because he was in the battleroid."

"Why didn't they ever send somebody to rescue him?"

"Well, the Conquistadors split up after that. The whole thing was an embarrassment, so most of the races don't even want to acknowledge the invasion took place, much less rescue anyone. But that's not all, Smitty was almost dead after the crash. He was dying in the middle of the desert."

"What saved him?"

"Well..." Fix's voice trailed off, half embarrassed and half worried. "Y'see, ya gotta keep in mind, Smitty didn't know where he was or what Earth was like. He was just trying to get out of the ship, when he ran into John Schmidt."

"Who's John Schmidt?"

"Smitty's John Schmidt. Well, he's half of him— Or all of him, really...kinda..."

Now I'm lost.

"This wandering bum named John Schmidt blundered into Smitty as he was climbing out of the ship. Smitty— In order to save his own life, kinda...sorta...absorbed him."

Whoa, I just gotta piss chill.

"Kaltherians have a taboo against consuming sentient beings, but Smitty didn't know. He needed the extra protein to survive anyways. That's why he's kind of a pathetic drunk sometimes."

"Hmmmm."

"He's spent the last fifty years punishing himself. Ya see, he didn't just absorb John

Schmidt's body, he's got his memories and, according to Kaltherian religious beliefs, the burden of his soul. So, it fell to Smitty to fulfill the hopes and dreams of the man he...kinda...killed. But ya see, he can't be the killer. It makes no sense."

"If its true, you're probably right," I admitted. "But maybe the guilt's drivin' him nuts. Maybe John Schmidt was a fucked-up, crazy serial killer."

"Then why wait fifty years to start? Nah, you're wrong. Besides, you think O.J. had a dream team, wait 'til you see the lawyers that appear if you try to charge Smitty. He's rich man, like F-U money to the tenth power."

"And he can look like anybody he wants to?"

"Pretty much.... Um, but its kind of an exertion for him. After he does it, he has to vibrate or something."

"What?"

"I don't the exact term for it. He usually just puts on the stereo really loud and stands next to the speakers. For him, it's like takin' a bath and getting a massage."

"That explains one thing."

"What?"

"Why he brought a boom box to the top of the bridge."

He sat real quite for a while, trying to think of a reply to that one. I didn't know how much of Fix's story to believe. Hell, for all I knew, Fix was an alien. Christ, you know I'm havin' a bad day when perps like Carl Cannon start to look normal.

The rest of the ride we spent arguing over the radio. Fix is the only guy I ever met who didn't want to listen to sports talk. He keeps beggin' me to put on this college station that plays nuthin' but screamin' mimis and songs about fucking the pope! Christ, what is he? Thirty? I thought you're supposed to grow out of that.

An hour later, we follow the limo into Atlantic City. What the Hell, the day's shot. Might as well get in a few hands blackjack. Fix is a Pai Gow player. Too rich for me. At twenty-five dollars a pop, is it any wonder he drives a piece of shit.

"What have you got against Japanese cars?" he asks me in the parking garage. "You wouldn't believe how long I've been drivin' the Nippon. If the odometer still worked, there'd be over a million miles on it!"

"One thing goes wrong in a Jap car and your talkin' an out of pocket expense of hundred dollars minimum. And they're too small."

"Oh, and what would you call cruisin' in style."

"I always liked Stallions."

"Give me a break!"

"They're an American classic and the parts are easy to replace."

"Yeah, that's cause they drop off every time you turn a corner!"

"Eh, forget it," I said, finally giving up. "What's Smitty do at these shows? What's he a comedian?"

"Nah, it's a sports card show. Football memorabilia and that kind of junk."

"Football," I said, stopping at the elevators. "Victor said the guy looked like Nate Jordan."

"Yeah, so?"

"My witness said the killer on the bridge looked like a football player. It's just weird, that's all."

I started to get on the elevator, but Fix put his arm in the way.

"Why didn't you tell me that?" Fix said kinda grimly. "I though we were working on this case."

"What? Like that's important? So what? Two witnesses describe a possible suspect or suspects in the same way. Carl Cannon kind of looks like Dick Butkus. It don't mean anything."

"It does," insisted Fix. "I didn't tell you how Smitty got so rich."

As we walked through the casino, Fix told me how Smitty or John Schmidt, wanted to be a football player. Using his talents, Smitty enrolled in college and started playing football back in the Forties'.

When he got to the pros, one of the talent scouts found out who he really was. The talent scout blackmailed him into working for him. If a pro got hurt or needed a vacation, Smitty would play in his place.

"You mean the football players *let* Smitty replace 'em?"

"Nah, they don't even know. Smitty's got this brain-eraser-thing he salvaged from his ship. They used to use it on abductees. One zap and you can rewrite your own memories. He let me try it once. You ever see the Pamela Lee wedding video? That's me."

"That's Tommy Lee."

"Not in *my* brain."

"How long did this go on?"

"Well, since they started doing drug tests, he had to slow down a lot. Then the talent scout died and— Well, it's not like he needs the money anymore."

"Did he play in a Super Bowl?"

"He played in *all* the Super Bowls. You should see his rings."

"So what's he doin' here?"

"Abe Tupper's supposed to do an autograph signing at eight, right? Well, the real Abe's probably relaxing on a beach in the Bahamas, while the Austin Rangers pay Smitty to do the signing. You see they—-"

"I don't wanna know anymore. You're gonna ruin my Monday nights."

We got the exhibit hall where "Tupper" was supposed to be signing. He was sitting in a side room finishing his lunch salad, while the PFL people talked with the exhibitors. I figured we'd just wait him out or tail him back to the limo, but Fix had to do it the stupid way. He pulled out his gun.

"Are you a fuckin' idiot? Put that away!" I hissed.

"I'm unloadin' it, see? C'mon, it's just a little payback. I'm just gonna scare him like back in the office."

I'm not above revenge, but this was a little much for me. I decided to sample the convention center hot dogs.

"We'll meet you there," added Fix, but somehow, I knew they wouldn't.

I bought myself a dog, but I skipped the mustard. Some twelve-year-old kid was sucking on the mustard dispenser like a thirsty man in need of a drink. By the time his mother pulled him away, I wanted to puke.

When I got back to the exhibit area, they were carrying Fix out the back unconscious. I guess Smitty decided to pull a reverse on him. He seemed like the type, not that I'm complainin'. Time to turn on the Goda charm. I walked up to the suit who looked like he had the most clout.

"Lt. Goda, Philly Homicide. You in charge here?"

"I'm sorry, you'll have to wait in line like everyone else."

"Hey, whose *that* guy?" asked Tupper, understandably shaken.

"Layin' it on a little thick, aren't we, Smitty?" I asked.

That seemed to jangle the nerves of Tupper and the suit. Suddenly, I was the center of attention. The suit nodded to two goons in blazers and they began to escort me to the mens room.

"Hey. Hey!" I objected.

The goons left me alone and the suit came in.

"Who are you?" asked the suit, now genuinely interested.

"Lt. Thomas Goda, Philly Homicide. I'm investigating a murder."

"Well, I'm sure someone will be able to account for Mr. Tupper whereabouts. If this leaks to the press—"

"Naw, he's not the suspect, Smitty is."

"Well, that doesn't surprise me."

"How so? And who are you?"

"Let's just say I protect the interests of the Profession Football League. We're like a secret service for the PFL, protecting it from the outside. My name is unimportant. But, if you like, you can call me Coach."

"Okay, Coach. If you're the secret service, is Smitty like your secret weapon?"

He laughed kind of condescendingly. Like, "Hey you don't know the half of it, buddy."

"Yeah, something like that. Smitty's sort of like insurance for the pros. Someone gets injured or can't play because of emotional stress..."

"And you just zap their brain and make them think they played?"

"We protect the players. Smitty can mimic anyone's style almost perfectly. The games would come out the same."

"Maybe. Or maybe some players don't want to shave the point score quite the way you want them?"

He didn't like that comment. A vein suddenly became noticeable on his forehead. What can I say? I got a way with people.

"What's he done now?" he asked.

"He's a prime suspect in the murder of six individuals. We're not gonna charge him, we just want to talk with him. You know where I can find him?"

"He was supposed to do the signing for Abe today, but at the last minute, he didn't show."

"How'd you know to get Tupper here?"

"Smitty's reputation is unreliable. My predecessor had better luck keeping him in line. Abe had a friend's wedding and a contract obligation. Oh, well."

"Well, if you see Smitty, you call me," I said giving him my card. "I'll find him either way."

"Lt. Goda, I've seen Smitty impersonate everyone from a Dallas cheerleader to the Fridge. Depending on his mood, he could be anyone, anywhere at anytime. You won't find him, unless Smitty wants you to. And these days, he doesn't like to be found."

Coach put my business card back into my front pocket and walked out the room. It's times like this that working for my brother in air conditioning repair seems like a real choice deal. I decided to hit the blackjack tables for a few free beers, while I decided if I should bail out Fix. I didn't have much choice. Stupid as he is, he was the only one who had a chance in Hell of finding Smitty.

CHAPTER 24 (Mark): The Devil in the Next Cell

I was so sure it was Tupper. Right up until the second his fist hit my nose. I should've known Smitty wouldn't be eating lunch unless it came in a bottle. The locals tossed me in a cell until they could run a check on me, the gun, etc, etc. Although I felt confident I'd eventually find Smitty and get one of his high price suits to keep this off my record (Hey, it was his fault), I didn't relish spending the week in a urine-soaked, cinderblock hellhole.

Then again, it might take me months to track down Smitty. They could take my PI license, and I'd have to get a day job again.

"Maybe jail isn't so bad," I said aloud.

"Don't delude yourself, Fix," said a voice.

The voice floated out of the darkness, like some invisible apparition, shrouding me in fear. It came from the next cell, which was extra dark since one of the hallway lights was out. The voice rumbled with a caged fury and spat like the sound of grinding gravel. I called him Jay, but that was probably the nicest thing he's ever been called. He's J.D. The Jersey Devil. And there's only one thing you need to know about him.

He's fucking nuts.

"This ain't jail," he said. "This is a crackerjack box. Any idiot can escape from here. Even you."

Jay sat in the furthermost possible corner of the darkness. I had never seen his face in the light and even though I was curious, I wasn't about to push for a view. Not in here. Thank God I'm in a separate cell.

"What are you doing in here?" It wasn't that I was surprised he was in jail, I was surprised it wasn't national news. The last time he ran amok in civilization, it cost the State of New Jersey about a billion dollars.

And they never caught him.

"Came into the city to take care of a little business. Nothing you want to know about, I'm sure. I played drunk to get in here. They skipped booking me after I vomited on myself."

I heard a noise coming from the floor, like a low moan. Looking down, I could see this huge Latino guy with tattoos and a bald head. He looked as if he had been beat up pretty bad. His head had been jammed in between the bars. I looked back at the scrawny

Jay.

"We had a little disagreement about the seating arrangements," explained Jay. "So what did you do, Fix? Feel up the coat check girl?"

"Pulled on a gun on Austin's quarterback and threatened to blow his head off for making me lose a football pool."

"That must've been some pool."

"Long story."

"You didn't let the locals find the Stuff on you, did you?"

Yeah, Jay knows about the Stuff. He was there the night I found it. That's not a long story, but I'd rather not discuss it. Okay?

"No, I'm not an idiot," I assured him. "As a matter of fact, I'm working on a very important murder investigation."

Jay laughed. And I thought his *voice* was creepy. He had this kind of joyless guffaw, as if he was laughing only to acknowledge my statement's potential for humor, not because he derived any amusement out of it. He slid into the light a little bit. I could see his worn sneakers and ragged jeans. The guy always looked like he was the last one in line at the Salvation Army. He turned his head away, as if he'd lost interest, until I opened my big mouth.

"It's true, some psycho with knives for hands is ripping out the livers of innocent people!"

Jay's laugh stopped short and I knew I was in trouble. Hell, just being anywhere in the vicinity of this guy was likely to get you shot at. He was taking an unbelievable risk just being here. Two years ago, he tore through downtown Atlantic City in a stolen snowplow and killed a suspected child molester. Although, according to Jay, this guy actually killed several children and dumped the bodies in a wooded area called the Pine Barrens.

Jay lives in the woods there (surprise, surprise). It's not like I wouldn't like to do the same thing to that sick fuck, but Jay was the only person to claim he had proof the guy killed the kids. He said the ghost of the dead children told him who the guy was.

Told ya. Nuts.

"Knives for hands?" he asked, although when he asked you something, it was more like a demand. "What are you working on?"

My instinct told me I should start screaming for the guard now. Then again, if Mindy wanted Viv's murderer in a box, I was talking to the right guy for the job. But manipulating Jay for my own purposes has never been easy. He's too smart. I needed more information.

"Why do you want to know?"

"Your killer," he said, trying to remember. "I think I've seen him."

CHAPTER 25 (J.D.): The Devil's Take

Normally, I never participate in Fix's nonsense. To align oneself with such incompetence is to invite error. And, so long as state and federal agencies continue to have my fingerprints on file, mistakes are not an option. But Fix has his uses, and so long as he holds that mysterious green jar, we are bound like two sides of a coin. I told him my tale.

My story began as it usually does; deep in the darkest grove in the Pine Barrens, on a wind swept night. The wind howled through the pines, as a gentle cloud of cold mist bathed the woods in damp and made everything smell of rotten wood and decomposing leaves.

The days were getting colder and I was contemplating my winter accommodations when I spotted her in a clearing. She was new to the Pines, her ghostly form only visible against the light of a full moon.

Fix, of course, does not believe in ghosts, which I find strange considering the circles he travels in. Then again, there is very little I believe about Fix sometimes.

As I stood in awe, watching the pale iridescence of her form waft in the gentle breezes of the woods, she turned and looked at me with a great sadness. Our eyes made contact and at that moment, I felt touched by this gentle spirit and her terrible loss. She drifted forward, like a leaf carried by a breeze and at once, I felt if I could just reach out to her— if I could just touch her wounded soul, that I could absorb some of the pain for her and maybe make her passing that much easier.

How wrong I was.

When she had closed the distance between us to the point where we could almost touch, her wounds became apparent. This was no gentle spirit, trapped in the cursed woods of the Pines. It was a banshee bent on revenge and its name was Katherine.

Katherine's touch filled me with such tumult and terror that I had to compose myself just to scream. Her life had been short, brutal, and a slow wasting away of the spirit by drugs and abuse. In the shadow of her soul I could see the cause of her pain and the man responsible for destroying what little spark was left in her.

We devils can see such things.

And, though I swore never to leave the Pines unguarded, and, though I vowed not to trust the ghosts that drift through this tainted forest, and, even as I repeated the vow to myself, I prepared to leave.

I took the guise of a human, as devils are often wont. I had just carved a new staff, which was sectioned in two parts that I could quickly screw together. Atlantic City authorities have never really gotten a clear picture of my human guise, but they know my staves. I call each one the Truth and carve its name in well-notched letters at the top. Atlantic City is the home of Leonardo Diaz, the man responsible for cursing another soul to eternal unrest. I shall find Diaz.

He shall know the Truth.

Somewhere on the highway beside a crowded campground, I managed to hitch a ride to Atlantic City. Its streets are, all at once, both sickening and comforting to me. Sickening, not because it is a towering Mecca of vice and avarice, but because its controllers have so blithely destroyed it. Comforting, because I know this is just the beginning. It is just one domino in a line of graft and corruption that will one day swallow this country — if not, the globe.

And when it happens, there will still be my Pines.

"Great-great-great-great, you're the caped crusader of tree huggers," interrupts Fix. "Are you going to get to the good part or what?"

I sit in silence for five minutes, watching Fix turn from impatient rambler to silent squirmer. A bead of sweat appears on his forehead and fear returns to his eyes.

"I'll be quiet," he mumbles.

I finish my story.

Leonard Diaz was part pimp, part drug dealer, part street hustler. Over the years, he had aligned himself with the local toughs, knowing exactly when to discount one of his "girls". But after he killed Katherine things changed.

He crossed a line he never intended to cross. The dividend of his investment in death finally shook him from the sophomoric, misspent days of his youth. He'd never be safe enough, never be mean enough, never be rich enough to stop.

The bar he was sitting in was built before the casinos. It had a deep, brown wooden texture that smelled of stale beer and cheap pot. Black and white pictures of the Steel Pier and a diving horse continued to dry rot in their frames.

The only other people inside were a jaded waitress, a bored bartender, Leonardo's "girl", a tall man in a raincoat and two of Leonardo's toughs. They were too young to be up this late, much less smoke pot in the booth of a dive in Atlantic City. The man in the raincoat was negotiating a price for Leonardo's "girl".

I moved to the bar and sat down, trying to think of the easiest way to kill him.

"Hey," he says, ever paranoid. "You lookin' for the shelter, man? It's down the street."

Leonardo and the toughs laugh. His girl sympathizes with me.

"Leave him alone. Buy him something to eat."

"I got some leftover stew," offers the bartender. "Maggie, get him some stew."

The waitress shakes her head and continues to smoke. Leonardo's "girl" does the honors.

"I'll get it. Jeez, you'd think you guys would sympathize a little."

When she gets closes enough, I grab her by the wrist and pull her close, my whisper like the harsh breezes of the Pines.

"If you are a friend of Katherine's, leave this place, leave this city and never return. Because what I'm about to do to Leonardo, he would surely have done to you."

"Get away from him, Wanda," Leonardo ordered, not hearing what I said. "He's crazy. You're gonna go with this guy."

"Oh, I don't know, Leo," she whined. "I feel kinda sick."

"You can be sick later, now go, unless you want this hand."

I pulled out my staff and began to screw the pieces together.

"Hey," said the bartender. "Hey, I don't want that in here."

I ignored him. Wanda began to leave with her "date".

"Aw, man leave him alone," laughed Diaz taking a drink. "That's probably his broom. He's like a freelance janitor."

Diaz and his cronies laughed, until I made the final turn of screw and the word "Truth" became prominently displayed. Diaz practically leapt out of his seat, his boys stood up and pulled out pistols.

"What're you, crazy?!" he demanded.

"I found this staff in the woods," I intoned. "I think it belonged to that Jersey Devil guy. Is it worth anything?"

I could hear the tall guy talking to Wanda. He was nervously asking about questions about her health. She was beginning to think he was a cop, but as he obsessed over the details of her personal hygiene, she decided to walk out the door with him anyway. (Nobody that weird could be a cop.) Diaz picked up the staff and his two boys put their guns away and relaxed.

"Oh, I don't know, man," he smiled, knowing he could probably get a good price for it. "How do I know it's authentic? How do I know the Jersey Devil really used it?"

"Because," I said, grabbing the staff and inching forward. "I'm using it now."

With one quick swipe, I knocked out the only light in the bar, but much to my surprise, the young toughs did not shoot, as I expected them to. They instead charged me, stumbling into me in the dark. I tossed one against the counter and the other against a framed picture of a lifeboat. It wasn't much of a fight, but Leonardo was out the door.

Charging through the bar's side door, I threw it open so hard it slammed against the side of the building, shattering its window and sending shards of glass all over the sidewalk. Leonardo was half a block ahead of me, running toward the lights of a Motel West. But, ironically, when he reached the door, he found the office closed and dark. Only the "No Vacancy" light was lit, a result of his earlier business transactions.

Charging past a sleeping drunk, I rounded the corner, hurling the staff. It got caught in his feet, causing him to stumble. Realizing I was upon him, he attempted to pull out his gun, but I stomped on his hand before he could raise it.

"Who are you man?" he whined unconvincingly.

"You left something in my woods," I growled. "Katherine sends her regards."

I picked up his pistol, fully intending on splattering his brains across the asphalt, but then I heard Wanda scream. In the great distance, in the fog of the boardwalk, I spotted the tall man dragging her onto the boards and toward a darkened enclave of benches.

It then occurred to me, that if I stop to kill Diaz, the gun shot would bring the police and I would have had to abandon Wanda to her fate. But if she died just as brutally and senselessly as Katherine, what was the point of my journey? I struck Diaz soundly across the head, hoping to knock him unconscious, but even as I turned and ran toward the boards, I could hear him crawling away.

Just as I reached the boardwalk, it started to rain. Bolts of lightning danced just off shore, while the casino lights continued to blink their empty promises. The tall man had pushed Wanda behind a row of pushcarts. He was hunched over her like some kind of animal. Lowing the gun, I aimed it at his head.

"Whatever you're doing," I hissed. "Stop."

The tall man turned around. His hands had somehow transformed. One hand was nothing but a pointed end which had torn open Wanda's insides. The other had been a knife, but molded itself into a hand which clutched a bloody prize.

And, when he turned, his face was bathed in the soft glow of a boardwalk lamp and I thought I recognized him. It looked like Art Lendelham, the late football player. Or rather, some twisted, evil imitation which had taken defensive lineman's shape. I let number 77 have it between the eyes.

The thing reeled back, dropping Wanda's corpse. The bullets passed cleanly through and already the holes closed like they were never there.

Wildly and with an inhuman speed, it's knife arm whisked at me through the fog. I was lucky to have ducked, rather than dodged, for the creature seemed to be able to overextend any part of its body, like some demented, psychopathic shape-changer.

I rolled and blocked and dodged, as the creature swung and stabbed and bit. It was all I could do to keep ahead of its deadly, reaching limbs. With no other choice, I threw myself off the boards and into the sand.

I stood up just in time to see the creature ooze out of its clothes, between the boards and onto the sand below. Its shape now mimicked my own, save for the soulless, silver pupils which stared back like sharpened daggers.

"You're quick for a filthy human," it laughed. "You must be healthy!"

I fled down the beach as fast as my legs would carry me. The wind kicked up and the rain and thunder roared. The creature continued its cruel imitation of me, elongating its legs so it could cover four of my steps to its one.

Then, just as it prepared to cleave me in two with one its distorted limbs, I dove behind an overturned lifeboat, firing as I somersaulted. The bullet struck the creature at the thinnest point on its overstretched legs. The thin membrane exploded and the part of its leg below the hit fell off, immediately returning to its original shape, which resembled some sort of black and green jellyfish. I landed on my back on the other side of the boat, as the creature howled in agony, flailing its distorted arms at me in protest.

Stumbling to my feet, I barely managed to run out of the way of the lifeboat, as the creature sent it tumbling after me. And, although it seemed injured, it had somehow shrunk to its human size again. At the same time, it shifted its wound to a more protected spot on its body.

"You disgusting little maggot! You will die a thousand times, human!" it swore across the beach. "Urgo shall consume you, body and soul!"

Scrambling, I managed to reach the boardwalk. As I stumbled up the wooden stairs, I noticed blood trickling down my left arm. I couldn't feel it yet, but it would only be a matter of time.

Leaping off the steps of the boards, I narrowly avoided the creature's hands, which pounded them to splinters. I whirled around, smacking the creature with my staff, which had little, but somewhat more effect than the bullets.

"Your very essence absorbed into mine," it continued to threaten. "Inside me, you will continue to exist only at my whim! You will know only a powerless existence, trapped in the bio-field of my anatomy. And when you beg for death, I shall ignore your pleas and let you wither into nothingness forever!"

The piece of boardwalk it was trying to climb up on finally gave way. The creature fell beneath the boards and I was running. But already it had oozed back through the boards at another spot in an attempt to surprise me. The rain now came down in sheets and I could feel my shoulder start to go numb.

But the creature was in far worse shape than I, not that that made it any less deadly. As it gave chase, it left tiny particles of green and black flesh behind, which was promptly washed away by the teeming downpour. I managed to climb the gaudy steps of the Taj, then ran across a ledge onto a neighboring hotel, stumbling and dropping the Truth as I did so. The hotel ledge was slightly higher than the upper level of the Taj, but as I rounded the other side, I realized that it was five stories above the beach. Below, the tide had pushed the ocean past the boardwalk to an empty parking lot below. Tiny angry, waves rippled across the parking stripes.

As the creature topped the steps, it began to lose its shape. My features, which it had copied flawlessly, now turned pale and transparent. Beneath its skin, tiny globules of liquid and flesh, danced inside its alien anatomy.

I had climbed onto a window washer's machine, which had been left out in the rain on the side of the hotel. Exhausted, the creature began reaching for me with fading enthusiasm.

"You're dying, thing," I snickered, trying to keep my distance. "Why don't you just ooze back into the sewer that spawned you?"

"Why should I?" it gurgled, trying to hold its shape. "You think you can kill me? You *disgusting* little man?"

Suddenly, it let loose a barrage of limbs from its body. In the same instance, I shot the support on the side of the machine. The bench plummeted five stories down, acting as a counterweight, pulling me skyward along the hotel's window. But the creature managed to snag my ankle at the last second and it, too, was pulled upward. I aimed the pistol at the ever-thinning limb around my foot.

"As long as one of us lives," it laughed, even as it died. "We *all* live."

I hesitated just a split second, in awe of its deteriorating, alien physique. The limb began to exude a mild acid, turning my sneaker into mush. I fired the last of Diaz's bullets and shattered the limb like a balloon full of jello. The creature plummeted, breaking apart and splattering against the wet parking lot below. The next wave claimed its remains and that was the last I saw of it.

Fix paced around in his cell, pondering this new information. I could hear the wheels turning in his head and, for the moment, he seemed to lose himself in the possible ramifications.

"How long has this thing been killing?" he muttered aloud.

"Does it matter?" I countered. "It must be stopped."

"Yes, well, as much as I enjoy your help and the inevitable police chase it usually brings, I think I got it covered," assured Fix with his dime-store bravado. "Besides I'm sure you're very busy trying to track down your latest, uh, victim. You don't want to get involved."

"I am already involved," I corrected. "This thing tried to kill me. I won't rest until it's dead. When I'm finished with business here, you'll help me track down this thing. And this time, I will kill it."

"Uh, sure, fine," Fix agreed, probably figuring I'd be searching for Diaz for weeks. "As soon as you finish your business."

Just then, the guard returned with a new prisoner. A prisoner who frequented the area, drinking himself into a violent intoxication, which inevitably led to this drunk tank. He stumbled into Fix's cell, passing out on the bunk closest to me.

"All right," the guard said to Fix. "You're free to go. I don't know why, but Tupper's lawyers dropped the charges, as long as you agree to sign a paper promising you won't come with in five-hundred-feet of him."

"No problemo," Fix smiled as he exited. "I hate football. Sign me up. Catch you later, Jay."

As Fix and the guard exited, a drunken Leonardo Diaz, shifted his weight on the bunk in the next cell.

See you soon, Fix. See you soon.

CHAPTER 26 (Mark): Where the Sword Don't Shine

"Thanks for bailing me out," I offered meekly, as I gathered my belongings and walked out the door with Goda.

"Don't thank me," he growled. "I woulda let ya rot. Ya smacked ass. They should take away your gun permit."

"Yeah? Well then why'd you come and get me?"

"I got beeped a few minutes ago. Victor's gone and there's another body."

Goda lectured me pretty hard about the gun thing on the way to the hospital, not that I really blame him. But you gotta understand, when you have a friend like Smitty and he happens to be a notorious practical joker, as well as a shape-changing alien — Hell, you have to fire a gun and burn down a building just to get his attention.

Last year, he imitated my dad and spent the day ordering me around the house. I mowed the lawn, painted the fence and washed the car before I realized the switch. Bastard.

I tried to grab a nap on the ride back to Philly. My cold still left me listless and congested. Goda was still pushing that Smitty was somehow the killer, which I had to admit, was a pretty plausible theory right now. I was even considering giving Smitty's ex a call, just to be on the safe side. Then, I walked into Victor's room at the hospital.

"You're not gonna believe this, lieutenant," the local detective said to Goda. "We had a guard posted right outside the door and no one heard a thing."

In the background, one of the uniforms took a picture of the empty bed next to Victor's. Seems his roommate was missing too.

When the detective lifted up the sheet on Victor's bed, I was expecting Victor's body. Instead, there was a young Japanese man, with a tattoo of Crying Freeman and the business end of a samurai sword sticking up his ass.

"Whoa!" I exclaimed, all at once shocked and impressed.

"Recognize him?" asked Goda.

"No, but he's definitely a Manga. What the Hell could've done that? And where's Victor?"

"We figure the Flayer and the victim arrived at the same time," the detective suggested. "His liver's gone, same as the others."

"But what would the Flayer want with Victor?" I pondered. "And why are the Mangas so anxious to kill him?"

"Why don't we ask them?"

"Nah."

"That's a very short answer."

"So?"

"So, I think you know somethin'. What do you got on the Mangas?"

"Nuthin'!"

The local detective went outside with the other uniforms, but Goda called after him.

"Hey, guys. You want to see a trick? My boy, Fix here does this thing with his eyes!"

I pulled him back inside and shut the door. You know, it's much more fun squeezing informants than it is being squeezed.

"All right, look, I'll tell you, but you gotta be careful with the information. You could get a friend of mine killed."

"Not on my beat. Spill it."

"The Mangas are a branch of the Philly Yakuza. One of the big men on campus is a guy by the name of Toxic Ito. He kind of started the whole anime theme in the tattoos."

"Anime?"

"Yeah, ya know. Anime, manga."

"How the fuck do I know what a *magna* is?"

"Japanese cartoons, ya ying-yang. Astro Racer, Arika, Mobile Suit Damgun. Top notch animation."

"So what's this to do with your friend?"

"He runs the Banzai Comic Book Shop in Chinatown. Deals in a lot of Japanese videos and comics. Every other Thursday, a group of his regular customers get together and watch a new release. Toxic Ito and his boys never miss a show."

"Perfect, that's tonight."

"No, wait! You can't just go barging in there. Ito will think Pierre blabbed it."

"Who's Pierre?"

"My friend who owns the shop. He took that name after he was naturalized. He's Korean," I explained. "You go in there and at best, my pal gets beaten up and his store torched. At worst he —"

"I know, I know. I worked the gangs for five years. *You're* gonna have to talk to 'em."

I didn't relish a confrontation with Toxic Ito. Without knowing who he was, I beat him in a Mystic card game tournament Pierre held at the store two years ago. That wouldn't be so bad, except earlier that same day, I helped Pierre forge a stack of rare and powerful Mystic cards for the store. When Pierre left the photocopier for a minute, I forged myself a copy of the cards and used them to win the tourney. If Toxic had been hanging out at the store, he was bound to have found out about it by now. Just as I was about to think of an easy way to explain the Mystic card game to Goda, my cell phone rang.

"Yes, Mindy?" I greeted, assuming the worst.

"Mark, could you run out and buy me more tampons?" squeaked Smitty in a very bad imitation. "AH, HA, HA, HAAAAA!! You're such an idiot, man!"

I stole a glance at Goda. He was standing the doorway, talking to a uniform. Smitty was babbling like the happy, obscene drunk that he was.

"Ha-ha!" he mocked, in a voice remarkably like a Simpsons character. "Thanks a lot for coming to the casino with me, dickhead."

"Where are you, *hon'*?" I asked, trying to keep up the illusion that I was talking to Mindy.

"Fluck you," he slurred. "Why? You wanna hang out, *babe*?"

"Just tell me where you are and I'm there."

I could hear Smitty knock over a couple of glasses. Somewhere in the background, a horse's carriage clopped by.

"You're not gonna like it. It's a bar," he mumbled, rapidly turning his tone to ugly drunk. "You don't even drink. *Why don't you drink?!*"

Goda finished talking to the uniform and was turning back toward me. I had to get Smitty off the phone before he suspected.

"I am very thirsty and will drink with you."

"You will?" Smitty slurred, incredulous.

"*Yes.* Now where do you want to meet, *sweetie*?"

"Uh, I'm not sure where I am. Let me call you right back."

"No! Wait!"

He hung up, probably forgetting the whole phone call in the process. Goda noticed my anxiety and gave me a bewildered look.

"We're gonna go back to the precinct and see if we can I.D. this stiff. You comin'?"

"Nah, I gotta run back to the office and get my car. I'll hit the comic book store around 7:30. If I don't call you by eight, swing by the store. If you don't see me, call this number. Ask for Sven and tell him I'm in trouble."

"Who's Sven?"

"My cavalry."

CHAPTER 27 (Narrator): Smitty Splits

Whenever Mark felt he was losing control of a situation, the image of Mindy's unraveling sweater came to him. Six years ago she had dropped a couple of tabs of acid, while sitting by the pool in his parents' back yard in the dead of winter. Mark was broke and just sat there playing Mushroom King II on his Atigo Hand Game. Mindy really wasn't doing anything, other than staring at the ice on top of the pool cover. Suddenly she started unraveling her sweater at a steady and dazed pace, leaving Mark to explain to his parents why his girlfriend was sunbathing topless on the deck out back in December. Yes, it was the same feeling that overwhelmed Mark now. The inevitable, helpless feeling that the next few hours were going to be worst case scenario.

Mark put on a good front for Goda, despite his flu-like symptoms, but he wasn't concentrating on the lie, so much as where Smitty's bar might be. As the P.I. left the hospital, Goda pulled his friend Darryl close, whispering instructions.

Hopping a cab, Mark let himself be driven around Independence Hall and the likely tourist attractions. After a couple of passes, he heard this horn behind him. The cabbie uncharacteristically waved the car ahead, but the driver didn't pass. Mark turned around. Mindy was following in the Nippon.

"Oh, for the love of — Let me out," instructed Mark, half embarrassed.

Fix paid the cabbie and got out. Mindy immediately pulled up along side the curb.

"What kind of detective are you?" she demanded. "I've been following you all day!"

"I saw you," Mark said unconvincingly.

"You did not!"

"I did too! I just wanted to see how long you'd keep this up," replied the aloof detective. "I thought you were getting your windshield fixed."

"It wasn't ready, so I drove down to Atlantic City and followed you from jail."

"What?! You drove the Nippon all the way down there? Jesus in a jackknife! Are you trying to destroy my car?!"

Mark's voice cracked, causing him to momentarily go into a coughing fit. He hacked up something and spit it into the street.

"It's fine," assured Mindy. "Disgusting and filthy, but fine. Get in, I'll drive you home. You look terrible."

busy. Can you just leave that here and take the train back?"

got a lead?"

"Min', just go home."

"Hey, I just saved you cab fare, the least you can do is let me come."

"For the millionth time, this is work! Not an episode of *Remington Steel*!"

"Mark!"

"No!"

"Mark."

"Uh-uh."

"Mark...please..."

Torn between love and duty, convenience and complexity, Mark's head swam with the consequences of letting Mindy tag along. But ultimately, when he looked into those eyes, they both already knew what the answer will be. Without even waiting for the response, Mindy parks and gets out of the Nippon.

"So, what are we looking for?"

"Smitty called me from this bar. I could hear the horse and carriages in the background. He must be in a bar along the route of the carriages somewhere. That's where we're looking."

"Oh," acknowledged Mindy. "Well, why don't we just get in a carriage and look for him during the ride?"

"That's —" began Mark, ready to belittle the obvious answer. "That's—Actually, that's okay. Yeah, we can do that too."

"On this very spot in 1776," said the bored carriage driver. "Thomas Jefferson wrote the early drafts of the Declaration of Independence. Few people know this, but a Tory assassin attempted to kill him during his final draft, but was stopped by a mysterious man known only as Patriot 13. The Spirit of Independence, they called him. Some say he was just a minute man. Some say he was an unstoppable giant. One historian even believes he may have been a Founding Father. Other say he is just a myth. Still others say —"

"Others say skip the history lesson," interrupted Mark. "We're looking for a bar somewhere along this route."

"So I can skip the schpiel?"

"Please."

"*Thank* you."

"This is nice," smiled Mark, trying to snuggle close to Mindy. "How come we only get to do this stuff when I'm on a case?"

"Because we never go anywhere other than your stupid office, the movies and the clubs."

"That's not true. How about that camping trip we took last spring?"

"All we did was hike in the woods and fool around! What kind of trip is that?"

"You're right. I hated the hiking."

"Jesus Christ, Mark! Will you stop fucking around?!"

"Geez, Min'. Tone it down, will ya? Don't turn this into another Delaware."

"Well, you're thirty fucking years old! Act like an adult!"

"What? What brought this up? I'm not the one who smokes pot like it's 1974!"

"You don't take anything seriously! It's always a joke with you! Our relationship— Viv dying—your career—you're like a little fucking kid who can't take responsibility for anything!"

"My career is not a joke! Okay?! I am trying to do *you* a favor— What the fuck is it with you?! Responsibility?! For what? I'm here for you, Min', who cares about anything else?"

"I'm s-sorry."

Mindy stammered over the word. She used it so infrequently around Mark, it was almost alien to her.

"It's just that, it's taken me all these years to get a perfect little circle of friends going. And now," she squeaked, voice shaking. "And now, without Viv, the circle's smaller and — I keep thinking about all the times you've been shot at — What if this thing gets you? It would be my fault!"

Mark's anger faded. As usual, Mindy didn't mean half the stuff she had said.

"Min', don't talk that way," Mark said, trying to console her. "I got the secret weapon, remember? Besides, given a couple of days, I probably would've made the phone calls, poked around and been sittin' right here anyway."

"Really?"

"Yeah," he assured. "Can I ask you something?"

"Mmm, hmm."

"At my funeral. Far, *far* into the future. When people line up to see me in the box there. Slip on a pair of nose and glasses on me, ya know, anything to lighten things."

Mindy laughed despite herself. Mark smiled, satisfied he'd turned Mindy into her old self.

"That is so rude!" she laughed.

"It'll be my last gag, c'mon."

"Okay," she smiled softly, looking into his eyes. "For you, anything."

Mark and Mindy snuggled close in the back of the carriage, missing several of the bars along the route. By the time they realized it, they were up past Twelfth Street, heading toward Broad at a steady clip. Mark insisted that the driver had gypped them, as if he expected the driver to interrupt them mid-hug to peer into one of the bars. The driver threatened to kick them off the ride, but Mindy relented and agreed to pay for a second ride, much to Mark's objection.

"You are so cheap."

"Cheap?!" Mark objected. "For a man of my financial standing I'm very generous."

"That's it," informed the driver several minutes later. "You've seen every bar along the route."

"Maybe Smitty went home," suggested Mindy.

"No, I don't think Smitty normally goes to this bar and he always likes to stay for last call. As he would say, that's the only way to tell a good bar."

"Well, I gotta get back to the stable," said the driver, still slightly annoyed. "My shift ended ten minutes ago. I could use a beer after this ride."

"Wait a minute," realized Mark. "Take us with you."

Across the street from the carriage stables was a little run down dive the drivers drank at called "The Horse & Buggy". It was caddy-corner from a parking lot, across the street from a building foundation full of trash and smack dab in the middle of the local crackhead traffic. Tina Turner's "Goldfinger" was blaring inside at top volume. Mark and Mindy got out near the parking lot. Mindy stopped Mark before he could cross the street.

"I almost forgot. I brought your cock."

Before Mark could bring the maximum puzzlement to the expression on his face, Mindy clumsily pulled his second gun out of her purse. Mark snatched it away, as if taking a bottle of drain cleaner out of the hands of a toddler.

"It's called a *glock*, Min'. And you don't even have the safety on. Are you trying to shoot yourself?!"

"I just thought — Well, I guess you were right about the killing thing. As soon as I busted open your strong box to get the gun —"

"You busted my box?!"

"Tch, will you let me finish? I'm trying to pay you a compliment. You were right. I thought about it and I can't kill."

"Well, I'm glad you figured it out before you burned down the office."

"That's why I've decided to hire somebody."

"Oh, God..."

Giving up, Mark crossed the street. Mindy followed, jabbering all the while about her intent to hire a hitman. The couple entered the dark bar, arguing in the usual fashion, until they both realized they were standing in the dark. The jukebox continued to blare Tina at a volume that made the speakers rattle.

"Hey!" screamed Mark.

"Ow, that's so loud," whined Mindy.

Mark held his ears, walked over to the jukebox and pulled out the plug with his foot.

"Aw, but I liked that song."

"Hello," called Mark, hiding his annoyed look from Mindy. "Anyone here? Smitty?"

"I'm going to use the phone."

Mindy crossed over toward the restrooms and the payphone.

"That's good. Call around. Get the best price for a hitman," sneered Mark. "Maybe they give discounts to lunatics like yourself."

"People do it," she insisted. "Don't act like I'm stupid."

Mark found the tavern owner, slumped forward on a table. A spilled bottle of vodka lay on the floor nearby. His grill, left unattended, sizzled with the remnants of a cheesesteak.

"Hey, yo, buddy? You awake?"

Without meaning to do it, Mark knocked the tavern owner to the floor. He flopped over on his back, exposing a large red gash across his belly. Mark snapped the gun out of his holster sleeve and onto the floor. He quickly picked it up and looked around.

"Mindy! Call the police!"

"Hey-hey!" Smitty greeted, suddenly exiting the mens room and wrapping his arm around Mindy. "Who turned off the music?"

Mindy screamed with a start, as Mark ran out of the kitchen and pointed both barrels at his drunken friend.

"Back away from her, Smitty."

"What the fuck are you doing?" laughed Smitty. "I didn't say you could bring her."

"Let her go," insisted Mark. "No one else has to die."

Bewildered and drunk, Smitty's head snapped towards Mindy.

"What is he talking about?"

"P-please," stammered Mindy. "Don't hurt me."

Mindy carefully met Smitty's gaze, as if he might snap her in two with a flick of his wrist. The look almost shook him sober, but he instead laughed and put his hands up. Mindy scrambled to Mark's side.

"Okay," laughed Smitty. "Now what is —"

As Smitty took a step forward, Mindy moved away and Mark cocked the hammer of his Barretta. Smitty laughed again.

"Just keep your distance," instructed Mark, curtly. "You're in a lot of trouble, Smitty."

"Tch, shut up," he scoffed. "Why do you always gotta — Tch, shut up."

Despite the darkness, Mark could see his friend was having trouble holding his shape. Smitty's limbs flopped, as if burdened with extra bags of skin. Becoming annoyed, he staggered back to his favorite bar stool.

"Smitty, the night of the club," began Mark. "Where did you go?"

"I told you, I was in Austin. Harold!" Smitty called for the dead bar keep. "Harold? Bring me two more cheesesteaks! Harold?"

"Did anyone see you?"

"I was playing friggin' football all evening, the whole fuckin' stadium could — YOUR RACE IS DOOMED HUMAN! — see me. Now sit down and put that away."

"What do you mean we're doomed?" asked Mindy.

"What?"

"You just said YOUR RACE IS DOOMED, HUMAN," explained Mark. "You sounded just like Dr. Evilski from the Inspector Frankenstein cartoon."

Smitty turned, looking at them in utter astonishment, despite his drunken haze.

"What. The fuck. Are you two. *Talking about?!*" he said, exasperated.

Mark gestured with his gun. Smitty peered over and spotted Harold's corpse, but as he did so, he also bumped into a nearby beer mug. It was filled half with beer and half with Harold's liver.

"Ahhhhhh!" screamed Smitty, knocking it over and stumbling backwards.

Mindy and Mark backed away a little further, circling around towards the exit. Smitty looked back at them in astonishment.

"Is he dead? I only passed out in the bathroom for — YOU SHALL DIE IN AGONY AND DESPAIR! YOU ARE BUT FODDER FOR THE GORNON FTHAL! — a minute... Why are you looking at me like that?"

"Don't you even realize you're doing it?" asked Mark. "Who's Gornon Fthal?"

"Gornon Fthall," Smitty repeated. "I know that name. Where do I know—"

Smitty turned his face toward the darkness, as if lost in his own thoughts. Mark's thumb danced on either side of the hammer and he could feel his scalp sweat under his hat. As he leaned forward cautiously, Mindy did the same.

Mark whispered, "Smitty?"

"FTHAL SHALL REND YOUR FLESH!"

The face of the alien had turned into something out of a horror movie. Suddenly sober and dangerous, it loomed over the surprised couple.

"Run Min'!"

But before either of them could do anything, "Smitty" smacked the end of a table, sending the other end up into Mindy's chin and knocking her unconscious. Mark fired both guns, but was swept aside by the creature's great strength. Mark crashed against the bottles behind the bar and almost immediately, Smitty returned to normal.

"—that name?" finished Smitty. "Hello? How'd you get over there?"

"Smitty," said Mark, trying to stay as far away from him as possible. "You got some serious, whacked out psycho playin' with the controls in your head."

"On the ship," he finally remembered. "Gornon was on the ship when it crashed.

How did you know?"

"I think Gornon's making a little bit of a comeback."

"Hey," Smitty said, finally noticing a hole in his left shoulder. "You shot me."

Mark made his way toward Mindy and tried to drag her away.

"Remember when you told me about Kaltherian anatomy?"

"That was a great strip bar, wasn't it?"

"Yeah. You guys are one big cell, right?"

"Basically."

"So you reproduce by, uh, osmosis or something?"

"I know what you're saying, but that can't happen," assured the alien.

"Then you got a serious fuckin' mood swing problem!" snapped Mark suddenly angry. "How do you know, huh?! How do you know that you didn't get fucked up one night and split in half?!"

"Because it don't work that way, Mark," Smitty said condescendingly. "Trust me, if I was going to divide, I'd know it."

"Fine," replied Mark reluctantly. "Help me get up Mindy and——"

Suddenly, Smitty started screaming in a loud, inhuman roar that shook the windows and left Mark standing there with his eyes open and his mouth agape. Somewhere outside, the carriage driver, decided to buy his beer elsewhere and changed direction. A perfect line shot right down the middle of Smitty's face and continued down his neck and under his clothes. Mark stared in morbid fascination, as Smitty's whole body became transparent and began to split, just like he had seen underneath a microscope in high school. Tiny globules of alien nuclei, aligned themselves on the split, then suddenly, "Rrrrrriipppp!", the alien's flesh was torn asunder. The sides of his head torn away, as the left and right sides went their separate ways.

Without taking his eyes off the transformation, Mark tipped over a soda with the barrel of his gun, which ran over the edge of the table. The soda and ice cubes clunked across Mindy's forehead.

"Mindy!" called Mark over the noise of the transformation.

Mindy sat up, but instead of screaming, she tilted her head to one side, unsure of what to make of the whole scene.

"Whoa," she gasped.

Finally, the right side of Smitty's body, now completely separated from the left, went limp, as the left side tore Smitty's suit in half. The left side balanced one leg, then used it's own mass to form a complete body. It now looked like Austin's running back, Sammy "Blackjack" Drapil, with silver, pupil less eyes and half a suit.

"Human," it growled in superiority. "Do you think you can stop me with *guns*? Do you think your bullets will *hurt me*?!"

Mark gave him a bored shrug.

"Both."

With a deft maneuver only seen in comic books and Jackie Chan movies, Mark lifted up one of the tavern's chairs with his foot and kicked it into the evil Sammy's direction. Just as it crested at his chest and began heading toward the floor, Mark started firing both pistols into the metal seat of the chair. The force of the bullets drove the legs of the chair through #21. He reeled back, screeching over the sound of the bullets and crashed into the jukebox across the room.

Mindy took it upon herself to scramble over to what was left of Smitty. Carefully, she lifted his half head to face her.

"Smitty?"

"Oh, man," he moaned out of the corner of half a mouth. "I really need a beer."

Evil Sammy, pinned against the jukebox, reached over and plugged the jukebox in. Tina Turner began blaring again, as "Blackjack" formed an extra set of arms, which burst from his hips. Each of his four hands grabbed the leg of the chair and pulled it apart like a wishbone.

"Ah, ha, ha, ha!" laughed Evil Sammy. "You can't kill me, human! If one of us lives, we *all* live!"

Mark was reloading his guns, when the running back started hurling chair legs with deadly force. As Mark attempted to take cover, the first chair leg pinned the flap of his overcoat against the tavern wall. Mark was forced to dodge the other three.

"Fuck. A. Duck!" Mark said with each hit.

Looking down at the holes in his torso, Evil Sammy forced them to close with some effort. He turned his sinister gaze toward Mindy.

"Need protein," he growled in determination.

Dropping Smitty, Mindy squealed in terror and ran out the nearest exit. Unable to stop her, the murderous alien turned toward the body of the dead barkeep.

"Protein," he growled again.

Mark tugged frantically, trying to pull his coat off. Across the room, Smitty's mass oozed and reformed the right side of his body.

"Smitty! Lil' help over here!"

Inside the kitchen, Blackjack put his hand across the grill, letting it absorb the charred cheesesteak meat, while the rest of his body oozed over Harold. Smitty, dazed and disoriented, struggled to get to his feet.

"It's no use, it's no use," he mumbled. "They're gonna kill us all."

Finally, Mark pulled himself free. Grabbing Smitty by the arm, he headed for the exit.

"What are you talking about?"

But before Smitty could answer, Blackjack began forming dozens of limbs. The limbs bored through the floor of the tavern, erupted through the floor and sealed the doors. Another limb shot upward through Smitty's body, skewering his head like a kabob.

"Ow!" he said in annoyance.

Mark instantly took it as a cue to move, narrowly missing being impaled. As the limbs started to burst from all corners of the bar, Mark blasted away. He jumped onto a table, then leapt to the counter and grabbed a bottle of whiskey from behind the bar. In the next room, he could see the distorted shape of Drapil, his oozing mass nearly three times its previous size and the pulsating limbs reaching through the floor and Harold's corpse like the roots of a demented tree.

"Your race is *doomed* human!" it taunted. "I shall feast on your *bones*!"

"Fuck-you-very-much," Mark quipped.

And with that, Mark tossed the whiskey bottle, shooting it in mid-air. The glass and whiskey exploded, igniting against the hot grill and turning the kitchen into a ball of flame. Evil Sammy's screech reminded Mark of Godzilla's roar, which he'd heard so many times watching Creature Double Feature on the TV back in his office. The running back's head dove into the kitchen drain, sucking the rest of its twisted mass with it. Mark fired blindly into the kitchen, even shooting a few times into the sink basin just to be sure, but it was gone. Mark ran over to Smitty, who was eating all the bar peanuts he could find.

"Need protein," he mumbled.

Mark spun him around, trying to shake him into focus.

"Smitty, you gotta help me!" Mark insisted.

"I can't, it doesn't matter," he mumbled in defeat. "We're all dead."

Smitty seemed overcome by a wave of depression, which caused him to momentarily lose hold of his shape. His head flopped to one side, then snapped back again. Mark shook him again, but it only seemed to make it worse.

"God dammit! Pull yourself together!" snapped Mark, not realizing the irony. "How do we stop this guy? Who's Gornon Fthall?!"

"My commander...in the ship..." he replied in a haze.

Smitty reached for another bowl of peanuts on the next table. Mark took the bowl and held it just out of reach.

"You can't kill him," said Smitty in exhaustion. "He's already dead."

Mark dumped the bowl of peanuts on Smitty's chest and he promptly absorbed them and regained most of his shape.

"C'mon!" he ordered Smitty, dragging him to his feet.

"Where'd you learn to shoot like that?"

"I live next to an arcade."

As Mark pushed Smitty outside, they were stopped by not less than a dozen armed Philadelphia cops. Goda, who led the force, aimed a gun and a loud speaker in his direction. In the background, Mindy was being cuffed and stuffed into a patrol car.

"Show's over, Fix," he boomed. "Drop the guns. You're both under arrest."

"But the real killer's in——"

Forgetting himself, Mark gestured with his guns, making the nervous cops cock their collective hammers.

"Sorry," finished Mark, finally stooping to set the guns down. "The real killer just dove down the drain. I know it sounds crazy, but——"

"Just drop the guns, Fix," Goda insisted. "It's over. You should've listened to me."

Smitty gave the cops little resistance as they cuffed him. Mark let the officers take his guns, but took a step back when they tried to cuff him. Smoke began billowing out the doorway behind Mark as the fire spread. In the distance, a fire truck siren howled. Goda gestured for the uniforms to leave Mark alone.

"What's that supposed to mean?"

"You missed the 7:30 deadline, we busted the Mangas."

"You what?! That wasn't the deal!"

"I didn't have a choice! I thought you were in there! I called your friend and he didn't show! What the fuck was I supposed to do?"

"You just wanted the collar!" scoffed Mark.

"You fucked up the deal when you didn't show!"

"Oh, bullshit! If you think you got the real killer in custody, you didn't even need to bust 'em! You suspected Smitty from the beginning and that's the only person you intended to pin this on!"

"He *did* it!" insisted Goda.

"Yeah? Well, I'm gonna hunt the *real* killer, *genius*! So fuck you and *fuck* your deal!"

Elbowing the uniform holding his guns, Mark shoved him aside, grabbed his guns and ran headlong into the smoke-filled tavern.

"Get back here!" ordered Goda. "Are you nuts?! You'll get killed in there!"

One of the uniforms attempted to follow, but Darryl stopped him. Goda limped over to where Mindy was sitting in a squad car.

"You boyfriend just ran into a burning building, you don't seem too worried," Goda sneered. "What's he up to?"

"Nothing," smiled Mindy knowingly. "Why don't you call him and ask?"

"Circle around the back," ordered Goda pulling out his cellular phone, much to Mindy's dismay. "Listen for the ring."

Inside, Mark had stumbled into the men's room, while holding the edge of his T-shirt over his mouth. One of the side effects from the Stuff, he discovered long ago, was that it made him completely fire proof. Unfortunately, that didn't mean he wouldn't suffocate once the air became too choked to breathe. Immediately, he downed an entire vial of the stuff.

"Oh, gaaaak!" he gagged.

Swallowing the green, glowing liquid was almost a feat in and of itself. Mark grimaced and winced, trying not to vomit. Bright green lights emanated from his eyes and mouth, while fog billowed out from nowhere, mixing with the smoke. Without even realizing it, Mark flailed with his arm, punching right through the wall of the bathroom stall and putting a huge dent in the towel dispenser.

Suddenly, Mark inhaled. Impossibly, his lungs sucked out all the smoke in the bathroom. With a cough, he exhaled a hard, grey block of ash.

"Ew," he said to himself. "I hope that's not the only effect."

As Mark completed his statement, he became aware of an intense stinging in his eyes. He snapped them shut and rubbed his eyelids. When he opened them, his eyes had stopped glowing but both of his eyeballs were completely black. What's more, Mark could see through the walls, floors, ceiling, his clothes and his skin.

"Cool!" he noted.

Carefully, he looked around. On one side of the tavern, he could see a Mindy skeleton sitting in a patrol car, while a Goda skeleton directed the uniform skeletons to surround the building. Then, in the distance about a block away, the oozing form of Gornon Fthall popped open a manhole cover and climbed out. When he reformed his body ten seconds later, he looked remarkably like a young, Trent Fredericks.

"Gotcha!"

Mark rushed forward, smack into a wall. He stumbled around, quickly finding the door and stumbling through a maze of blazing tavern furniture that he couldn't see. The phone in his pocket began to ring.

Outside the back, Darryl and Vincent cautiously made their way around the back of the smoking tavern. Darryl heard the phone ringing, gestured to his partner, then aimed his gun at the nearest door. Suddenly, Mark burst out of the door with his overcoat engulfed in flames.

"Ahhhhhh, help me!"

"Drop to the ground!" ordered Darryl. "Drop to the ground!"

While Darryl and his partner tried to pull a blanket from a nearby dumpster, Mark ran right past them and down the alley. Discarding the overcoat, he beat out a small fire on the top of his hat, laughed smugly, then ran into a telephone pole. Young Fredericks was still a block away, walking south and still unaware of his pursuer. Unfortunately, Mark thought he had a clear shot and lifted his gun to fire. The few civilians in the area, fled in random directions. Unfortunately, Mark couldn't see the block of buildings between him and the malevolent alien. His bullet bounced harmlessly against a brick building. The shot caused Gornon to increase his speed to a slow jog.

"Shit!"

Mark started running across the street, but then heard a screech. All he could see were the engines of vehicles hovering in mid-air, while skeleton drivers honked angrily and skidded into invisible obstacles. Opening and closing his eyes, he tried to shake the vision from his gaze. Behind him, two of the police skeletons were giving chase on foot, stopping briefly at one of the accidents.

Stumbling over the median, the detective tripped his way across the street, nearly getting run over by a seven-foot skeleton on a custom Harley with the name Jonny Plazzz, etched in gold letters on the gas tank.

"Odin's eye!" boomed Sven from the motorbike. "You've rousted the ire of the blue guards! Quickly!"

With one hand, Sven threw Mark onto his bike and peeled away.

"I came as soon as I could," explained Sven. "I was with this most remarkable young woman. A contortionist by trade, she——"

"I really appreciate the assist, pal," interrupted Mark. "But I got a big problem. We — Oh, shit."

"What is it?"

Mark was looking through his left hand. Strange black and green globules were cruising through his veins, slowly working their way down his arm. They were concentrated in the center of the back of his hand, right where Victor's syringe had hit him. Even Mark's remedial detective skills put that one together.

"Victor, you're a dead man," he cursed to himself.

"What was that lad?"

"Never mind. Turn left here."

Sven made the turn. Mark could see Gornon three blocks away. He was watching the pedestrians on Spring Garden Street, looking for someone to carjack.

"The Son of Thor is yours to command!"

"Great. Ya see Smitty's-been-accused-of-murder-and-he's-really- an-alien-from-another-planet-and-the-guy-we're-after-is-actually-the- murderer-but-he-didn't-exist-until-Smitty-split-in-half-and-we-got-to-catch- him."

Sven sort of looked away, pondering in utter confusion. Mark could see the wheels spinning fruitlessly in his brain and decided to just tell him in words that he would understand.

"Um, we're after a demon."

"Ah, ha!"

Sven gunned the bike with one hand, while gesturing dramatically with his sword in the other. Mark held on for dear life. He briefly recalled the day Sven purchased the cycle and the small jet engine they had to install so it could move Sven's massive bulk. The Asgardian whipped around the corner, just as Gornon/Fredericks was about to rip the spine out of an unsuspecting hatchback owner.

"That's him!" pointed Mark.

Gornon turned and frowned menacingly.

"Foul creature! Taste the sword of Asgard's Favorite Son!"

As Sven passed, he swiped as Gornon's head, which opened up on the side, letting the blade pass harmlessly through. The swing passed so effortlessly, Sven dropped his sword and momentarily lost control of the bike. As he wobbled, Gornon broke a "No Parking" sign off at the sidewalk and hurled it into the spokes of the back wheel. The whole bike seized and the twosome crashed into a closed pizzeria, destroying the display window and a couple of tables. Fortunately, Sven's near-invulnerable hide took most of the burnt of the accident. The mighty godling sat up, looking bewildered.

"Did I just slay Trent Fredericks?"

"How do you—? Oh, right, St. Paul Vikings. Sure, I get it. You okay?" asked Mark.

"Don't be a fool, Fix. Of course, I'm fine!" boomed the Asgardian.

"Well, you're the one that told me you turn mortal if you lose your sword."

"*Lose*, lad, *lose*. I *know* where the sword is."

By the time Sven and Mark had climbed out of the pizzeria, Gornon had oozed into a parked Caddy. Letting his arm seep into the ignition, he formed a key, started the car and began driving away. Sven looked around for his sword in a panic.

"Well?! Where's the sword, *Hercules*?!"

"It was right here!" insisted the perplexed Asgardian.

Sven spotted the hilt of his blade in a nearby sewer.

"Balder's balls!" he muttered, thrusting his arm inside.

The handle was just out of Sven's reach. Mark looked back and forth between Sven and Gornon's stolen car. In frustration, he began stumbling down the street again.

"We're gonna lose him!"

Spotting Mark in the street behind him, Gornon/Fredericks made a right and then another, hoping to quickly lose him. But Mark could still see through the buildings and ran the distance down the street in between. As he reached the intersection, Philadelphia patrol cars skidded into his view, quickly jamming the road with cars. Almost instantly, Mark was surrounded by cops again. A Caddy tried to veer onto the sidewalk to get past the cars, but ended up smashing into fire-hydrant. Mark tried to follow Gornon/Fredericks, but then, abruptly, there was a sputtering sound and his vision returned to normal.

"Get on your knees!" barked Goda through a loudspeaker. "Put your hands above your head!"

"He's in the car!" insisted Mark as he complied. "For Christ's sake, he's right here!"

Darryl and his partner made their way to Gornon's stolen car. A jittery old man, a bloody gash on his forehead, carefully got out of the car. Mark's mouth dropped opened in shock. Mindy stuck her head out of the patrol car.

"Oh, my God," she gasped. "You almost killed Jimmy Stewart!"

"It's all right, sir," assured Darryl, helping the confused octogenarian away from his smoldering Caddy. "We'll get you to a hospital."

"I am so sorry," Mark apologized to Goda. "He's in a car just like that, I swear."

"Save it for your arraignment, jackass. Put 'em in with his girlfriend."

By the time Goda drove back to the precinct with his prisoners, he looked like he should have steam coming out of his ears. He even thought about taking Mark to a certain abandoned building in North Philly and beating some sense into him. Just as they reached the station, Mark's X-ray vision started to sputter on and off. He didn't notice it at first, but Mindy did. Across the street, four men in suits got out of an unmarked car and approached.

"Oh, crap. Mark. Eyes, eyes!" she hissed.

"Shit!" added Mark, trying to hide his face. "We can't let them take us out of the car until it wears off!"

"Like I could stop them."

The old man, who had been bandaged at the scene, got out of Darryl's patrol car and prepared to go inside to file charges. The four men approached Goda.

"Lt. Goda," said the leader. "Agent Garden. We understand you have the Flayer in custody?"

"Yeah, you can help us get him inside."

"We have orders to take him with us. Captain McLane already approved the paper-work. We have a special holding facility reserved at the Liberator Compound."

"Oh, that's good. Here he is."

Goda appeared to give up his prisoner easily, but used the moment to get behind the four officers and aim his pistol at them.

"Don't fuckin' move!" he screamed.

"Lieutenant!" squeaked Vincent in surprise.

"They ain't feds! Fix calls them Colonials. I call 'em, fuckin' stupid if they think they can pull this shit twice on me. Get their weapons."

"I'd think twice before I followed that order," Agent Garden informed Darryl. "Lt. Goda here is throwing away his pension. Don't do the same."

"You're the one who's fucked, G-man. McLane's not even on duty today, so any paperwork you got is bullshit! I'm gonna book you myself you dumb fuck!"

Just then a beat-up, red pick-up truck with mag wheels and a bullet ridden 4 by 4, sped into the parking lot and jammed on its breaks. Instantly, all heads turned toward the noise, as an angry J.D. stepped out of the truck. His torn and taped Chuck T sneakers stomped the asphalt, as if they were punishing it. His tattered trenchcoat couldn't hide the sawed-off shotgun and staff. From beneath his bandanna, he barked his demand, "STEP AWAY FROM THE OLD MAN!" The Colonials took advantage of the distrac-tion to draw their guns, causing a Mexican stand-off right in front of the police station.

Mark sat next to Mindy in the back of the patrol car. He sighed in frustration, as if this would finally top off an already shitty day. Goda and company aimed back and prepared to fire.

"Reach into my purse," she hissed. "I got handcuff keys, see if they fit."

Mark struggled and managed to reach the purse.

"How did you get these?"

"You know I own a pair of handcuffs," she mumbled half-embarrassed.

"This is just like that time in Delaware," he lamented.

"Give it a rest," sneered Mindy.

"Give us the Flayer, Goda," insisted Agent Garden. "Or we'll end this right here."

"All of ya! Drop it! Now!" Goda barked back. "The old man is under our protec-tion!"

"Yeah?!" screamed J.D. from across the street. "Take a good look at what you're protecting! TAKE A LONG LOOK!"

Goda stole a side glance at the old man, who was cowering behind a patrol car near Darryl. Then, he did a double take. In the commotion and with the bandage on his face, Goda didn't recognize him without his famous coach's hat. As they made eye contact,

Goda gasped, "Lance Trubor." Trubor's confusion drained away and he stared back at Goda sinisterly.

Only J.D. and Goda could see the monster rise up and transform its head into a hideous maw of fangs. Goda fired, but his bullets were too small. J.D. let loose with the shot gun, injuring Gornon/Trubor, but causing the police to fire back. A bullet winged his arm, as he pulled back from the onslaught. The police and the Colonials were suddenly in a gun fight.

Gornon/Trubor let the bulk of his shape ooze into a gray pillar, which knocked down Vincent and two of the agents. It smashed its way into the driver's seat of Mark and Mindy's patrol car, reformed as Cory Rothinger and drove away. J.D. was instantly in hot pursuit.

Inside the car, Mark almost had his cuffs off. The former quarterback for Philadelphia formed a second face on the back of his head and a third hand to put on the radio at maximum volume.

"You're coming with me, bags of protein," it informed them.

Mark angrily kicked the grill into the second face of the monster.

"Fuck you, Cory! God, I've-always-wanted-to-do-that," announced Mark on behalf of Philadelphia football fans everywhere.

The patrol car sped erratically through the streets of Center City. Up sidewalks to avoid traffic, then skidding back onto the road without any heed to possible pedestrians. The Cousin Kevin song from "Tommy" was blaring on a local radio station. Finally, Mark got his hands free.

"I'm *so* glad we traded you." With that, Mark grabbed Mindy and rolled out of the patrol car on the next corner.

Battered and bruised, Mark staggered to his feet, with one cuff still on his left hand. Mindy tried to roll out of the gutter, but to no avail.

"Get me outta these!"

"I think I dropped the key."

Just then there was a sputtering sound and Mark's X-ray vision kicked in again. He couldn't see Mindy at all.

"Where are you going?! I'm over here!"

"Just keep talking, I can't see you."

J.D. skidded to a halt, opened a door, pulled Mark inside and sped after Gornon/Cory anew.

"Don't you dare, Mark! Don't you dare!" she called after him.

Mindy looked around the gutter, at the broken glass, the weeds growing out of the sidewalks and the abandoned buildings around. She also noted the silence and the deserted streets. She was handcuffed and lying in the gutter, with no visible means to get the cuffs off or even get back on her feet.

"You know," she finally said to herself. "This *is* just like Delaware."

On separate streets, the Colonials and cops pursued Gornon/Cory, barreling down the streets of Center City as fast as their vehicles would take them. Gornon/Cory turned the wrong way on a one-way street, then ran up a sidewalk to avoid a car and nearly ran down a man at a sidewalk produce stand. J.D. gunned the red pick-up on a parallel street, cutting across a small park to try and cut him off.

"How did you know?" asked Mark, as he held onto the dash for dear life.

"My friend Diaz worked for the Flayer. He lured victims to a doctor's office in Ventor for the Flayer to kill."

J.D. was going so fast, he crested a small hill, momentarily putting the pickup in the air and skimming a traffic light with the top of the cab.

"Shit-jesus-shit!" said Mark in absolute terror.

"I checked out the address, but it was deserted. Found a delivery receipt for some medical supplies delivered to a place up in Darby. I was on my way over, when I spotted the commotion in the parking lot."

"And?"

"My secret shame," he shrugged. "I'm an Austin fan."

J.D. lost sight of Gornon/Cory as they reached Penns Landing. J.D. had taken the upper ramp, but Gornon was already turning onto Delaware Ave below. He was cut off by the Colonials.

"Down there!" screamed Mark. "Down there, they're — Oh, my God!"

As they watched, Gornon/Cory prepared to do battle, but much to his surprise, the lead Colonial changed shape. He now looked exactly like Victor and the other Colonials' eyes were as silver as mercury.

"Ha, ha!" laughed Gornon/Cory. "If only you had revealed yourselves at the station— Well, no matter. The invasion begins anew!"

Victor raised an alien-looking device at Gornon/Cory. His silvery eyes widened with fear, even as he turned to flee.

"B-but, I am Gornon Fthall!"

Victor pressed a tiny button and a thin blue line of light struck Gornon/Rothinger as he tried to ooze down the nearest sewer. His distorted form instantly froze on the spot. One of the others shot the ice mass, blowing it to pieces.

"Sorry, Commander," Victor said sadly. "You're already alive."

As Victor turned to leave, something undulated under his shirt. Victor paused, concentrated a moment and it disappeared back into his body.

J.D. tried not to lose his patience as he navigated the traffic towards the fleeing car below. Philadelphia wasn't his turf and he needed Mark to cover his tracks if the police got too close. Mark's vision had kicked in and he could clearly see the four Kaltherians for what they were. His mouth babbled, while his brain tried to grapple with the consequences aloud, much to J.D.'s annoyance.

"There's four of 'em?!" squeaked Mark in utter astonishment. "There's four of 'em?! Five, if— No! Smitty makes six. SIX?! Where the hell are the guns?!"

"Shut. Up." J.D. instructed, stifling the urge to slap him.

Mark rooted around inside the truck in a panic, finally opening up the glove compartment. It was full of water balloons.

"What-the-hell-is-this?!" he demanded.

Unaccustomed as he was to explaining himself, J.D. bit his lip again.

"I'd suggest you be careful with those."

"What are we supposed to do? Soak their clothes and hope they're too embarrassed to invade the Earth?!"

J.D. turned and scowled, explaining slowly through a mouth full of grinding incisors, "They are filled with *Napalm,* you idiot!"

Victor and the other Kaltherians made a break for the nearest highway ramp, but an earlier accident had snarled it with traffic. Just as it looked as if the red pick-up was catching up, Lt. Goda and Darryl skidded across Delaware Ave. with Smitty in tow. Victor took a hard left and swung back into the city, while J.D. followed right on his tail.

"Get a balloon ready," he ordered Mark.

Taking one of the shimmering tubes of liquid, Mark rolled down the window with one hand and held the balloon as if it were a dead animal. J.D. nashed his teeth, punched the accelerator and rear ended Victor's getaway car.

"Now!"

Mark, more startled by J.D.'s yell than anything else, made a hurried, wild throw, barely clearing the truck. The balloon took a nosedive on a Beamer and exploded into a ball of flame. The Beamer's car alarm wailed in distress.

"Sorry!" Mark called back to the car.

Just then, the trunk of Victor's car popped open and two of the Kalterian/Colonials sat up inside, aiming machine guns at J.D.'s windshield. He pulled Mark down with one hand, veering right with the other.

"Get down!"

As the Kaltherian/Colonials filled the air with bullets, J.D. turned his truck up a short flight of stairs leading to an out of the way mini-mall with a glass elevator and an outdoor cafe. Patrons scattered, as J.D.'s truck plowed through lawn furniture, smashed through a kiosk, then charged over another flight of stairs, landing with a crunch on the street on the other side.

"Man, do you know what your insurance premium will be after this?!" said Mark, trying to hide his panic.

"No," J.D. replied flatly trying to shut him up. "It's not my truck."

"Well, you're not gettin' the keys to *my* Nippon, mister!"

Just then, on an intersection ahead of Victor, two patrol cars skidded to a stop. The officers positioned the cars slightly staggered, between the buildings on either side of the thin street. Gornon/Victor didn't even slow down.

"Urgo," he ordered.

And with that, the Colonial in the seat next to him broke out a portable rocket launcher in a matter of seconds. Urgo/Colonial oozed the upper portion of his body onto the roof of Victor's car, positioning himself dead center on the roof. Aiming the launcher, he armed the explosive and fired. The two patrol officers dove out of the way, as the rocket exploded between the two patrol cars, clearing the way for Victor to barrel through. Urgo/Colonial oozed back into his seat.

"Flawless as always," commented Gornon/Victor.

"Thank you, sir," acknowledged Urgo.

Goda was driving with one hand, while spitting orders into his radio with the other. Unfortunately, most of the available units had converged on the intersection with the exploded patrol cars. Traffic then conspired to jam up everyone, except the Kaltherians.

"I don't freakin' believe this," simmered Goda, the stress nearly boiling over. "C'mon! C'mon!"

"Would this be a bad time to tell you my handcuffs fell off?" asked Smitty.

"YES, it would."

"I don't want to cause any trouble."

"Just shut up!"

"Lieutenant," said Darryl, gesturing to a coffee house.

The local java hut was on the corner of the snarled intersection. It had two windows, one on either corner, which reached to the floor and were roughly garaged-sized. Goda repositioned the car, immediately getting the hint. Smitty made a confused face.

"You know, I could use some coffee too, but..."

"Oh, no," said Goda unconvincingly. "I'm losing control of the squad car."

Goda jammed the pedal to the floor, sending the car up the sidewalk, through the windows and past the traffic jam on the other side.

"Whoops," he added as he crashed through.

On the way through, Smitty had snagged himself a steaming cup.

"Mmmm," he said warmly. "Latte'."

At the same time, J.D. was weaving in and out of traffic on Broad Street, zooming toward City Hall at a dangerous speed, while taking potshots at the Kaltherians. By the time he shot one to pieces, the other would pull himself back together and return fire. Mark couldn't take a chance on another throw, the vehicles were moving too fast.

"This is stupid!" shouted Mark. "You're gonna run out of bullets or roadway!"

"Hold the wheel! I'm jumping over!"

"Are you nuts?! You'll never—!"

But before the twosome could begin their argument, a seven-foot tall Asgardian popped out of a manhole a half block in front of the Kaltherians.

"For ASGAAAAAAARD!"

While Mark was bouncing around Philadelphia, Sven had climbed into the sewer to get his sword. It slid down further down a darkened drainage pipe by the time he found a big enough entrance to get his bulky muscles inside. He promptly got lost in the darkened sewers, only to emerge at this convenient spot sometime later.

Gornon/Victor jammed on the breaks, but it was too late. Sven had planted himself firmly in the middle of the road, holding up one foot to stop the car. The impact wrapped the entire manifold around his leg. Inside the car, air bags deployed, saving Gornon/Victor and Urgo. But in the back, the only thing that burst were the two Kaltherians against the trunk lid.

"Shit!"

J.D. couldn't stop in time and barely managed to veer the truck right. It skidded and smacked both wheels against the curb, than flipped up half a flight of steps, a mere one hundred feet from the nation's largest municipal building, Philadelphia's City Hall.

Urgo and Gornon/Victor began to run, but Gornon turned back toward the Asgardian, hurling a baseball-sized, semi-transparent globule at him.

"Leg," he instructed.

The tiny blob promptly attached itself to Sven's leg and began sending phony messages to his nerves and muscles. Sven's leg locked up and he couldn't get his balance to pull it out of the manifold.

"Demon!" he cursed. "Stand and fight!"

Mark stumbled out of the wreck of the truck, but J.D. was already out and on his feet, searching the dispersing crowds furiously for the aliens.

"You see 'em?!" he demanded.

"Yeah, yeah, give me a sec."

Sven was trying to pull the car off his leg, while in the trunk, a quivering mass of green and black goo attempted to separate itself and hold a form. J.D. tossed in a Napalm balloon and it erupted into flame.

"Now see here!" objected Sven. "My foot's stuck in there!"

"Fix! Where?!" demanded J.D., ignoring Sven and growing impatient.

Mark scanned the area. One of the locals, carrying an enormous boom box, caught his attention. It was blaring "Naughty by Nature" to everyone in a two block radius. Nearby, Victor/Gornon and Urgo had already morphed into an elderly Oriental couple and were attempting to board a bus.

"There!"

J.D. charged across the street and God help anything that got in his way. At that moment, Darryl and Goda skidded to a halt nearby. Without skipping a beat, J.D. somer-saulted over the car, putting all his momentum into one mighty blow of his staff. For a split second, Goda pictured the old man's head exploding like a ripe melon. Instead, the staff pushed in the top of his head, as if it were made from a thick, syrupy jello.

"Jesus Christ! It's one of 'em!" exclaimed Goda, looking back at Smitty. "Can't you recognize your own kind?"

"Hey, sometimes I get up and I don't even recognize me."

J.D. was thrown off balance for an instant, but it was instant enough for Urgo to grab him by the throat.

"*You* again!" he snarled. "Get your filthy appendages off me, you primitive!"

Urgo pushed J.D. so hard that, when he landed against Goda's opening car door, he forced it shut and cracked the window. Mark was trying to catch up with the commotion. All he could see were panicky skeletons, as he tripped his way into a hot dog vender and down the sidewalk.

"Urgo!" Gornon's voice bellowed from the old woman. "Quickly! The bus!"

Morphing their appendages, Urgo and Gornon used their own bodies as leverage and tipped the bus toward the squad car. J.D. rolled out of the way, while Goda and Darryl scrambled out the passenger side. The entire vehicle went over with a crash. Gornon took the form of Victor, while Urgo took the form of a sinister J.D. Smitty oozed out of the driver's side window and was disgusted by the carnage.

"Gornon, you're a real *asshole*, man!"

"Rojbor," Gornon/Victor smiled in smug delight. "Where's all your pretty words and mores, now, hmmm? I'll bet you're just as sick of these humans as we are."

"Leave 'em alone!"

"Or you'll what?" mocked Urgo.

Behind him, Goda and Darryl took up positions behind the patrol car, while Darryl radioed for paramedics. J.D. was a little disoriented, but took the time to recover his staff. Mark was slowly picking his was through the bottleneck, which had accumulated in the area. The center of the city of jamming up with cars.

"You can't hurt us. You took a vow of non-violence, *philosopher*," Gornon/Victor taunted, using the word as if it were a curse. "Come with us. There's still time."

"Don't die with these filthy animals," urged Urgo.

"Dammit, the invasion is over!" insisted Smitty. "We crashed! We lost!"

"Poor, naive Rojbor," laughed Victor/Gornon. "That was all part of the plan."

J.D. had circled around, but not far enough. He charged Urgo, but Urgo was ready. A second pair of appendages burst from his body at a weird angle, pinned J.D. to the ground and pointed a shotgun at his head.

"No!" insisted Smitty.

At the same time, Smitty lunged, using his own alien reflexes to push the gun away. The barrel swung away, but Urgo fired anyway, blasting Victor/Gornon's gun to pieces. Frustrated, Urgo shoved J.D. into Smitty and fled with Victor/Gornon. The twosome elongated their legs and waded through the traffic like it was shallow water.

Mark was closest and tried to pursue, stumbling through the crowds and the cars. His sight started to wear off and all he could see were dozens of panicking naked people.

"Oh, man," he lamented, even as he ran through what looked like panicky overweight, naked locals. "Join a gym people!"

Sven, a radiator still attached to his leg, made several heroic leaps, leaving his footprint on several hoods. When he finally caught up to the twosome, they were heading into the Reading Terminal.

"Stand fast!" ordered Sven. "Or face the might of Asgard's favorite son!"

Urgo extended his arm. He had concealed several weapons inside his body. With a small effort, he pushed a .357 magnum through his arm and into his hand. He fired at Sven and the bullets ricocheted off his invulnerable chest.

"Ha! Your bullets cannot harm me, mortal!"

Even before he finished the sentence, Urgo lowered the pistol and fired a shot into Sven's groin. It didn't penetrate, but he collapsed like a house of cards. Victor/Gornon and Urgo continued to run. Mark followed at a distance, stopping briefly to make sure Sven was okay.

"You okay, Sven?"

"Fine. Just don't touch me," he squeaked.

Mark was wheezing by the time he reached Arch Street. J.D. ran up behind him and grabbed him by the collar.

"Where?!" grimaced the relentless hermit.

Mark made an exasperated face and looked around. The effects of the Stuff were at an end and his head was making fizzling and popping noises. Finally, he caught a glimpse of the two Kaltherians shoving their way into a club, known locally as "The Troc".

Relieved to be in his element, Mark was recognized by the bouncer from his band managing days. J.D. charged in headstrong, while Mark took a second to make excuses. A concert was in full swing and the band, The Nude El's, was whipping the mosh pit into a frenzy.

Outside, three black Beamers with tinted windows pulled to a stop. Several Oriental men in suits and overcoats, slipped out of the cars. Moving swiftly, each cradling something under their jackets, they moved in and around the club.

Mark caught up to J.D. inside and grabbed his arm. J.D. nearly turned and took his head off. He felt completely out of control in this place.

"There's only two ways out besides the front!" screamed Mark over the music. "One's backstage and the other's upstairs! Let me go backstage! I used to know these guys!"

"What if they go out the front?!"

"I told the bouncer to stop anyone that tries to leave without a hand stamp! It's the best we can do! Go!"

J.D. shoved his way through the groups of drunken college students. Mark tried his best to get the attention of the security guys, but he didn't recognize any of them. Shoving his way closer to the stage, he attempted to get the lead singer's attention, hoping to stop the music, at least for a minute. The guitarist was in the middle of the solo and when Mark's eyes met the singer's he immediately recognized him.

"Hey, Fix!"

"Hey, man! I need your help!"

Unfortunately, the only reason the band remembered Mark was from an incident four years ago. Mark had scammed the only good-looking group of female groupies at a "Battle of the Bands" in Los Angeles. He had convinced the girls to come back to his band's hotel room by telling them they were actually the Nude El's. As soon as Mark got up on stage, the lead singer kicked him hard in the face and into the mosh pit. The dancers were packed so close, even someone as heavy as Mark was easily supported.

On his back, with a dusty sneaker mark across his face, Mark could see up into the balcony section. J.D. was searching for the two Kaltherians. Mark spotted them in the balcony, away from J.D. Unfortunately, they had spotted him and decided to ambush him on the left side of the balcony.

Stepping on heads and shoulders, Mark staggered his way to a thick group of power cables, which were part of the lighting set up. He climbed up into the balcony, poking his head up in time to scream, "Look out!"

J.D. ducked just as Urgo lunged with one of his appendages. He over swung, which forced him off balance. J.D. charged at the Kaltherians, knocking them into each other. Mark added his weight to J.D.'s push, forcing all three of them into a fire stairwell, evening the odds.

Unfortunately, in the dim lighting of the Troc, no one could see that this exit had been clearly sealed, for reasons that became obvious once it was opened. The fire exit was on the third floor and led nowhere, except to empty space. Mark held onto the fire exit's handle, while J.D. was caught on Mark's feet. Urgo was wrapped fairly tightly around J.D., but Gornon/Victor let himself fall.

Almost immediately, Gornon pulled himself into a ball, letting his clothes drop away, while transforming into a hawk and flapping away. Urgo was oozing all over J.D., attempting to consume him.

"You're mine, human!"

"I hope you like me well done."

J.D. grabbed the last two balloons out of his pockets.

"Jay, no!"

He pulled off of Mark's feet, allowing himself to fall with the Kaltherian. They landed in a dumpster below, which burst into a fireball a few seconds later. Mark pulled himself back into the building. Behind him, no one even noticed the commotion, while below, all he could see was a ball of flame. As Mark turned to leave, he ran smack into the Manga boy that had confronted him at Viv's apartment. His face was livid and full of rage, as if he were holding back every fiber in his body from killing Mark.

"You let Victor get away!"

Before he could respond, Mark felt the dull, metal handle of a sai thwack him on the back of the head. The music and the lights faded into blackness.

<u>CHAPTER 28</u> (Mark): Toxic Ito Collects

As if I didn't feel crappy enough, these reject ninjas go and whack me upside the head. I suppose I should've been wondering if Jay had made it out alive, but I had a nasty feeling my own personal safety was more in jeopardy. (Besides, Jay survived that plane crash last year in the Everglades and that was much worse. I won't bore you with the details, but in involved this Haitian cult, a dinosaur egg and a Winnebago. Long story.)

When I came to, the distinct smell of bubble gum was in the air, along with the musty smell of old cardboard and magazines. I would've sworn I was in Pierre's comic book shop, until I opened my eyes and saw all the expensive office furniture.

Toxic Ito's workspace looked like the office of an extremely successful Japanese comic book geek. It was filled with boxes of expensive comics, signed manga memorabilia, framed animation cels from Arika and Mobile Suit Damgun.

Short, squat and balding before his time, Ito sat at his desk rifling through a stack of poorly drawn comic books. One of his goons stood ready with a comic bag and backing board. As soon as he was done reading the latest issue of Robfield's *The New Bloods* it would be socked away for posterity. Probably for some federal agents to seize and steal, when his luck finally ran out.

"You read any Robfield, Fix?" he asked upon seeing me stir.

"I prefer Frank Miller, actually," I said snobbishly, noting the plastic restraints on my wrists and ankles. "Robfield's just another comic book fanboy with a bankroll and a computer colorist."

Ito carefully closed his colorful piece of crap, then slid it into the bag without bending its spine.

"Make sure you put two pieces of tape," he instructed his flunky as it was sealed.

Ito was like that. He had to have everything just right. His boy had probably bagged half of his warehouse-sized collection, but I'm sure he repeated his instructions with every single comic book he sealed. Like a lot of collectors, he broadcast his anal-retentiveness with every smug word and gesture he created.

"Now, let's see. You owe me some Mystic cards."

Oh, yeah. And he was a sore loser. Big time.

"Sorry," I said blithely. "I didn't bring my deck. I lost it all in a crap game to a twelve-year-old, if its any consolation."

"How unfortunate."

"That's what she said."

Toxic reached into his desk and carefully pulled out two decks of Mystic cards. He gestured for two of his goons to move me closer to the desk. One of them cut my hands loose.

"These two decks are the exact some cards we were playing with the night of Pierre's tournament. I remember every card. I have a mind for such things. Shuffle your cards and give me your best game."

"Or?" I asked.

"I'll have your hands cut off."

Then he forced a laugh, although I couldn't tell if he was amused by my reaction or the thought of my reaction. Mystic tournament play is a best out of three. And, as you can imagine, Toxic took me in two straight games. With every move I'd make, he'd grumble, but with every move, he made, he added his smug little laugh. It wasn't enough that he was winning, he had to win, beat you in a new bold move and humiliate you all at the same time. Such a tiny little man, such an immense ego.

"Now," he said quite pleased with his victory. "That history has been corrected, let's talk about Victor."

"Victor is not who you think he is."

"We know," he said as condescendingly as possible. "Why do you think we're trying to kill him?"

"He owed you money," I said rather obviously.

Playing dumb fed his ego. His eyes lit up every time I opened my mouth. Hopefully, he'd keep me alive, so I might tell others of his vast "intelligence".

"Everyone owes me money," he said, bored. "You don't get paid by killing them. No. Victor, and several of my other dealers, have fallen victim to a kind of plague."

"Plague?" I said, genuinely astonished.

"Don't play dumb, Fix," he whined.

Now, I was in trouble. Since he was convinced I knew something, any rejection of that would appear as if I was hiding something. And, since I didn't know what he was talking about, I couldn't very well make up a convincing lie.

"C'mon, Hwan saw you talking with a woman who was part of the experiment."

Viv. He was talking about Viv. Now it was all clicking in my head. Viv had that postcard from the people who do the medical experiments. Ito's boys must've been following Victor and saw me in the club talking to him and Viv.

"Experiment?" I continued to play dumb.

"Hwan's brother, Victor and his lady friend all went to the same testing lab," said Ito impatiently.

"That's the connection!" I realized, standing up and nearly losing my balance. "I'll bet all the Flayer's victims had been tested at the same lab!"

I was met by stony silence and an awkward pause.

"You're going to kill me after this, aren't ya?"

"Well," he replied, unsure. "We did finish our game. And, we know where the testing lab is."

"Darby."

"No, it's in Jersey."

"Then the place you need to go is in Darby. They put the address of the Jersey testing lab on the postcard, that would lead people right to them if they stayed there."

I sat back and smiled, rather pleased with myself.

"What's the address?" growled Ito.

"You'll never find it," I mocked. "I better take you there myself."

Ito forced another laugh, as if he were cool with my one-upmanship.

"Follow his directions."

"Yes, Oyori," obeyed Hwan. "And should we kill him afterward?"

"Only if he's wrong."

CHAPTER 29 (Mark): Die with your Disc Player on

On the trip to Darby, I began to feel sick again. Fortunately, I managed to convince Hwan to stop at a Castle Burger on the way. Marching to your death is hungry work, after all.

"Is this it?" Hwan growled at me, rolling to a stop in front of a desolate looking building. He seemed to have a personal grudge against me. I barely looked up from my bag of fries and tiny hamburgers.

"That's the place," I said a little too confidently. "I'll wait in the car. This is a bad neighborhood."

"That's okay," smiled Hwan, roughly pulling me out of the car. "We're bad neighbors."

Hwan and his two goonish sidekicks escorted me to the front door, as if they expected me to have a key. After giving me a nasty look, Hwan forced the door open himself and we went in.

The hallway was painted in drab, two-tone green. The floor had that old, very worn cheap tiling and the ceiling was riddled with a series of pipes that seemed to go to all the rooms. I was trying to observe possible clues in the debris and dust on the floor, but my escorts weren't so subtle. Hwan had, at some point, untelescoped his telescopic ninja sword. Despite the suit, he looked like a really cool character from Immortal Combat. I gotta get me one of them swords.

"This is a big building, so let's split up. I'll got with Daphne and Velma and you go with Scooby."

Hwan ignored me and peered into the first room on the left. It was empty. I finished a burger and dropped the box on the floor. One of the goonish sidekicks gave me a look.

"What?" I said in disbelief. "You run around killing people and *that* upsets you?"

"You shut up, Fix!" insisted Hwan, the tension showing in his neck. "After this, I kill you myself!"

"As long as it's done by a professional," I quipped. "Can I have a sword?"

"Shao," Hwan gestured to one of the goons. "Check the next door."

Shao made the same, slow, cautious movements, then finally kicked the door in. If these guys were gonna kill me, I'd wish they wouldn't keep me waiting. Shao gestured for everyone to go in. They were taking it way too seriously and ducked in the door as if they were expecting a whole battalion of monsters. I rolled my eyes and let myself be dragged in.

"Closet door," whispered Hwan, as if he were diffusing a bomb. "Shao, you watch the other door."

Paranoid about traps, he insisted I open the door. Nothing. The only thing odd was that half the room was taken up by an indoor storage tank, which looked rusty and unused. It smelled like gasoline and at one time had "U.S. Army" stenciled on one side. Even I realized there was nothing here. As they carefully crept their way to the next door in the hall, I reached in my pocket for a vial of the Stuff. Fortunately, I had one left. Unfortunately, I realized then it must have broken in my pocket, probably while I was running around the Troc. Oh, fuck.

The last room was just like the second, it had a storage tank, a closet and looked pretty empty. Hwan gestured for me to open it, then stopped and grabbed my arm.

"Don't!" he hissed. "It *trap*."

"Well, you wouldn't want me to get hurt before you kill me."

"I don't want to see building blow up with me!"

"Where's the trap then? I don't see it."

Hwan gestures to a small piece of string caught in the closet door.

"That's not a trap, that's just string."

"It trap," insisted Hwan.

"It's not a trap!" I said more exasperated at Hwan's stupidity than the fact he was going to kill me. I looked at Shao. "You tell me. Is that a trap?"

"I don't see a trap," he reluctantly agreed.

"You don't have to see trap," Hwan insisted. "I give orders here."

"Excuse me," I said in my best antagonizing voice. "Who are these guys, chopped liver?"

"You do not order me," corrected Shao. "And I see no trap."

"Oyori give orders to Hwan," corrected the other goon. "You must obey."

"I cannot obey my eyes do not see!" insisted Shao.

"That is trap!" insisted Hwan.

As the threesome argued, I considered my options. I'd never make the door that we came in, they were standing right in the path. There were no windows in the room that I could jump out of. I looked at the closet door. Maybe, just maybe, it wasn't a closet at all and led to another room. If I could lock it behind me fast enough, I might be able to get away. I took two steps and opened the door. It was a trap.

The floor opened up beneath us. Shao and the other goon landed on a bed of spikes at the bottom of a ten-foot deep pit. As he fell, Shao tried to pull out his pistol, which landed on the edge of the pit near me. The closet doorknob came off in my hand and I dropped it and caught the edge of the pit. Hwan made a spectacular save of himself, by doing a split in mid-fall, jamming his extended legs against the walls of the pit and balancing himself with the sword on the bottom. He was just inches away from death.

"Well, it looks like I owe *you* a beer."

"I kill you Fix!"

There was no leverage for me to climb up and I just didn't have the upper body strength to pull my fat ass up. But I managed to bring my eyes to the edge of the pit. My left hand was throbbing unnaturally, like a cheesy special effect. What the Hell is wrong with me?!

"Look, if I can push myself off of you, I can get out of here and then I'll pull you up. I won't let you kill me, but you can call me names."

"No!" the stubborn Japanese spat defiantly. "I rather die in pit!"

What a jerk. And after all that money I spent on Japanese stereo equipment. Then things got really weird, someone that looked amazingly like quarterback Mick Jeremy without a shirt, peered into the pit. Since I was losing my grip on my left hand anyway, I snatched up the gun and aimed it at him.

"Pull me up or you're——"

Before I finished, the quiet Kaltherian grew about sixteen arms, which sprouted hands and guns of various calibers.

"Not you Mick," I said sadly to the four-time Super Bowl winner. "That's just *wrong*."

"Throw down your weapon, human," said evil Mick in a very ominous, deep voice.

I was loosing my grip and set the gun back on the ledge just in time to hold on with my left hand again. In a few minutes, I'd have to let go. Evil Mick walked away from the ledge and I made one last heroic pull to see where he was going. He moved to the side of the room, but as he moved I could see that he wasn't even a whole person. The bottom half of his body was squashed up in a bucket.

"Bucketman," I said aloud.

"Bucketman?!" said Hwan incredulous. "You about to die and all you say is Bucketman!"

"There's a bucketman up here, okay? I'm dyin' I can say what I want."

Bucketman pushed a secret button hidden on the wall inside a section of flaking paint. Part of the room slid away and behind it was a wall of complex machinery and video monitors. The monitors surged to life. Most of the screens were connected to stationary cameras around the perimeter of the building, but the largest was some kind of video conference link. The room on the other side of the video looked like some kind of computer room, which was under construction. Suddenly, Victor walked into the camera's view.

The twosome began talking, but I could only understand about half the words. Hwan, apparently, couldn't understand any of it.

"...in six hours..." I caught from Gornon/Victor.

"...already prepared...instructions?" I caught from bucketman.

"Knew it was trap," muttered Hwan. "What is noise?"

"Shhh!" I insisted.

The cheesy effect continued on my hand. A tiny grey/green blob forced a portion of itself out from under my fingernail. Now I understood everything.

"The meeting with the Liberators cannot be rescheduled!" insisted Gornon. "You must avert your cellular degeneration or destroy yourself. In either case, destroy the building, we won't need the excess fuel."

"The storage tanks," I whispered to Hwan. "They must've held some kind of fuel for their ship."

"What is he going to do to us?" asked Hwan, still straining to stay up.

"Yes, commander," Bucketman continued. "The tall, thin human looks perfect for absorption."

I looked back at Hwan's tall, thin, lanky frame. No sense worrying him.

"Uh, he says he's gonna let us go."

"The stadium will be ready within one rotation. Confirm retrieval beam."

Suddenly, a beam of white light shot down through the ceiling, as if it was passing through the roof above. A small, gold and green disc appeared on the consol next to Bucketman.

"Hey, Victor! I'm gonna shoot your pathetic *punk* ass!" I shouted from across the room.

Gornon looked my way and smiled.

"Ah, Fix. Your friend Victor is dead, human."

Gornon opened his shirt. Victor's face came out of his chest, looking like he was in agony.

"Help...me..."

Gornon willed Victor back into his body.

"And so shall you join him...in *oblivion*!"

"Is that north of Trenton? I hate long commutes."

"Make sure that one *suffers*," Gornon added, looking at Bucketman. "Good luck, pool brother."

The screen went black and Bucketman picked up two nasty looking syringes. He turned and noticed the goo leaking out of my hand.

"I guess you won't be needing this," Bucketman said in my direction, putting a syringe down.

"What did he mean by cellular degeneration?"

"It won't matter in a minute," he explained.

His arm shot across the room and he injected Hwan in the neck.

"Ah, stop!" he protested.

"Hey! Knock it off!" I insisted, concluding that whatever it was he was doing, couldn't be good. I reached for the gun.

"You can't kill me, if one of us lives—"

I slid the gun around to face the bucket.

"No, wait!" protested the Bucketman.

I fired a few shots across the floor. They pierced the bucket, which began to bleed black and green all over the room. Bucketman howled in pain, as he features began to distort.

"No! I was so close!" he moaned.

Stretching in the other direction, he reached for a lever that on the console near the video monitors. I figured that couldn't be too good either. I turned to Hwan, some kind of weird, cloudy goo was pouring out of his mouth and out of the tiny hole the syringe made in his neck.

"Fix..." he pleaded. "Help...me..."

Concluding he was a goner anyway, I pushed off of Hwan, lifted myself up and tumbled away from the pit. His body made a cracking sound and, as I pushed off, he fell forward onto the spikes. His head split open, oozing cloudy goo everywhere. I stood up just in time to shoot off Bucketman's arm, which had just reached the lever. The weight of the severed limb pulled the lever down. Bucketman's insides continue to leak out of the bucket, deflating his body like a punctured balloon. Cautiously, I walked over and looked into the bucket. The face of the world's greatest quarterback was on the bottom.

"Okay, face boy, I want answers!" I insisted. "What's Gornon's plans and what the hell is this in my hand?"

"By this time tomorrow, Gornon will be running this whole *planet*. But you won't live long enough to see it, human."

"Why's that?"

Even as I asked the question, I became aware of a distinctive beeping, coming an area just below the console. It looked like a time bomb, which was counting down numbers from twenty-seven.

"But, you'll be —"

"If one of us lives, we all live."

I was four floors up and I'd never be able to run outside in time. Without hesitating, I went over to the bomb and pulled out a wire. The timer stopped.

"Hey, hey!" I said excitedly. "First try!"

Unfortunately, I could hear the same sort of beeping coming from the next room. I ran to the sound, found the bomb and pulled out the same wire.

"You'll never get all four!" taunted the Bucketman.

Down the hall, through a couple of rooms and at the top of the closet, I found the next bomb. I pulled out the wire at twelve seconds.

"Crap!"

Back down the hall, up a half flight of stairs and I burst into the next room. Unfortunately, the floor had partially caved in this room. I fell into the room below and was precariously balanced on another crumbling floor. Across the darkened recess, I spotted the bomb, illuminated by its digital read out. I thrust the gun out and fired in the vicinity of the wire. The timer stopped at seven. I happily sang a few notes from the Agent 007 Theme.

There was an audible beep, as the bombs reset themselves in unison. The timers now all read twenty seconds.

"Hey! What sorta sadist wired this place?!"

When I turned around, a wave of cloudy, transparent goo was filling the hallway just above. Inside its mass I could see the decaying forms of Hwan and the other Mangas. The Bucketman had gotten caught up in the wave of slime, and the bucket was carried along.

"That's it," cheered Bucketman. "Go after the protein, little Kalther. Ha, ha, ha, ha, ha!"

"Man, this is worse than the warm up act for Gwar," I said aloud.

I couldn't get back up. I opened the door, but the goo had already begun oozing down in the hall below. I scooched along what was left of the floor to the other side. I looked outside the window. I could see a street lamp and Hwan's car parked right below. I picked up the bomb.

"Little Kalther? Is that stuff an extension of you? Is that part of Gornon's plan?"

"Better get used to seeing it, human, soon your skies will be *filled* with it!"

"Well, I'll give you a head start."

I tossed the bomb and jumped out the window. The bomb landed on the face of Bucketman.

"Mmmm!" he said in protest.

I managed to catch the street lamp with both arms, just as the building exploded. My weight bent the front of the lamp in half, slowing my descent and dropping me onto the roof of Hwan's car. I rolled over onto the street and shielded myself from flying debris. It was then, I realized, I was even luckier than I thought.

"Hey, this is *my* gun," I said aloud, examining the pistol. "How lucky is *that*?"

CHAPTER 30 (Smitty): The Alien had a Chapter

Americans are weird, you know? I've been one for, I don't know, fifty years, and all I ever hear them talk about are three things: Sex, their personal hygiene, and crime. They want to get fucked, need to be clean and will do anything to stay out of jail because you can't get the first two in prison. At least not how you want it. Man, this police station stinks. I need a beer.

"You can talk now or later, makes no difference to us, John," said the one legged cop in front of me. "We can wait here all day."

"You can't hold me here," I said flatly. "Even if you could arrest me, I could slip out of this place anytime I want to."

"Look, John——"

"I'm not John," I corrected. "Smitty. Fuckin' say Smitty."

"Whatever. You wanna bust loose, Freako? I probably can only slow you down, but your buddy, Fix. I'll hang his ass out to dry as an accessory."

"You can't do that."

"Maybe not, but it'll keep him in court for a couple of years. Eat up his money. Probably get his P.I. license suspended. You got all the money in the world, but him? He don't got the sense that God give him, much less a bankroll. So what's it gonna be?"

Fuck. This is all I need. The world's ending and now I gotta explain it to everybody.

"All right, but bring your boys in here," I instructed. "I don't want to have to explain it twice.... And... Can I get a beer?"

Goda brings in his Barney Miller rejects. The Captain, a black guy with a tailored suit, walks in like he owns the place.

"Smitty, I'm Captain McLane, I understand you can shed some light on what's been running amok in my city."

I got a bad vibe from him. Like he was gonna give me instructions. I hate when people give me instructions.

"I changed my mind, I want to see my lawyer."

"You don't get a lawyer, Smitty," he explained. "You are an illegal alien, in every sense of the word. And since the federal authorities have already tried to kill you once, I suggest you tell me something interesting."

"You're not like the nice black captain on Homicide, are you?"

"Hell no. I'll kick your ass," he smiled broadly.

I briefed the cops as much as I could. Don't remember much and considering what happened to me, they should be glad I could remember anything.

My home planet is called Kaltheria and, like Earth, it's seventy-five percent water. Unlike Earth, the other twenty-five percent is made up of Kalthers, our great elders. Giant ameboeas the size of continents. The whole ecology of our planet revolves around their care. It's nice, from what I remember.

All of our technology is bio-energy based, so we traded with other sentient worlds to get space technology. We're actually very good at building stuff, once we get the materials. I even built myself an ionic parameter containment vessel. You wouldn't know what that does, but, trust me, everyone was very impressed when I built it.

Now, don't get the impression I'm an engineer or a tech; my training was almost zilch in that area. (Which is why everybody was impressed.) I was—I am, for lack of a better term, a Philosopher. Next to High Priest and Military Commander, this was one of my people's most respected professions.

Then Betelguesians came. These guys are short, little, hairless assholes with big eyes. (They also come in an assortment of loud, day glow colors.) They had formed an alliance with some other warlike races. They called the group, the Imperial Conquistadors, and vowed to rape and pillage the universe.

Our elders aren't very warlike, but there was a lot of misinterpretation during the negotiations. Our Elder Kalthers, who eat constantly, thought the I.C. was searching the galaxy for more food for them. The next thing you know, I get drafted.

My ship carried a contingent of one-hundred and forty-four Kaltherian soldiers, including Gornon Fthall, the commander, Urgo, his second and Glorbitt, the high priest. There was a real good reason for that many crew members, but I can't remember why.

"You're going too fast," interrupts Captain McLane. "Take your time and think about it."

"I... I can't remember."

"Can't or won't?"

I guess I was sounding pretty frustrated. Normally, I'm a great actor.

"How about that beer?" I ask.

A bulky cyber cop, with half his torso and left arm replaced by metal, walks into the room with a soda and pops the tab with his metal finger.

"Sorry, all we got is Treska," he says.

"C'mon, Jack," says Goda, as I take a sip. "How long's that shit been in the machine?"

I take a sip of this "Treska" anyway. It taste funny. Flat, sweet. I get a little tingle and hey—-

"I remember something! An experiment! On the ship!"

The Captain eyed me suspiciously.

"No, no, really!" I insisted, gulping the rest down. "Gornon was a bio-engineering genius! He did something—I can't remember now."

"Gene," says the Captain. "How much Treska is left in the machine?"

After everyone in the room emptied the change in their pockets, I began emptying the Treska machine. Goda said something about it being pushed under the stairs behind other, more popular vending machines, but I wasn't listening. Standing in the middle of a pile of empties, it all came back to me.

Gornon discovered that Kaltherian DNA is very easy to manipulate, since it's so big. He encoded our DNA with the genetic information of our shipmates. Now normally, when a Kaltherian reproduces, it creates a smaller version of itself, much like humans do. But Gornon's engineering rewrote the reproductive instructions. When we split, we were recreating each other!

"So let's assume what you're telling us is true," summed up McLane. "You split and recreate Gornon. He can split all his own. What does he need you for?"

"I don't know," I admitted.

"Fix said when you crashed in the desert, you ended up absorbin' some guy. Maybe that screwed up Gornon's experiment," added Goda.

"And if you can absorb someone, what's to stop Gornon from replacing policemen or government officials— My God, Tommy, we're talking a global threat here!"

"Yeah, we're all dead," I agreed sadly. "Can I get a beer now?"

But McLane was already ignoring me. He strode back into the ready room handing out orders.

"Gene," he said to the bulky half cop, half machine. "Take Smitty here to forensics and come up with a blood test so we can spot these aliens. Raymond, alert dispatch, I want to be notified of *any* possible sighting of these things. And Tommy, get Jonny Plazzz or whatever the Hell his name is, on the phone to the Liberators."

Then, out of the blue, Mark walks into the room. Strides right up to McLane with all the confidence in the world, just like I taught him.

"Where the fuck have you been?" begins Goda.

"Long story," they repeat simultaneously.

"Listen, McLane. I'd hold off calling in the Liberators, right now. A sighting of a large group of them might cause a panic."

"Well, I'm open to suggestions. Smitty just briefed us."

"Gornon's the leader. I overheard some of his plans. Where's Sven?"

"I think he's in forensics."

"I'll be right back. Don't do anything."

"But—"

"Give me one second," he insisted, striding out of the room.

"He seems awfully sure of himself," commented the captain.

"Yeah," I agreed and realized at the same time. "And how did he know the captain's name?"

<u>CHAPTER 31</u> (Narrator): In the Next Room...

In the next room, Mindy finished answering the questions of the desk sergeant, but no one would answer her one question. What happened to Mark? Wandering around the police station, she found Jonny Plazzz talking with Dr. Gulacy, the police forensics specialist. They were examining the tiny globule which had so easily paralyzed the leg of the world's mightiest hair stylist.

"Speak plainly, doctor of forensics Gulacy!" insisted Jonny. "The Son of Thor knows not of your genetics and dee-en-ae."

"Jonny?" interrupted Mindy. "Did the police say anything about Mark? I don't even think they're looking for him."

"Lady Mindy, I beseech you. Make the words of this mortal make sense to thine ears!"

Gulacy sighed and rolled his eyes.

"All I'm saying is, that what paralyzed your leg was a genetically engineered one-celled organism."

"Like an amoebae?" asked Mindy.

"Yes!" continued Gulacy, happy to have someone understand him. "It was designed to paralyze the cells of nerve endings. The thing is still alive, so presumably, they can multiply and we could make more. In theory, we could use them, if we found the right stimulus, and activate them."

"Who could engineer something like that?" asked Mindy.

"No one on this planet, pardon the expression."

"Well?" asked Jonny, anticipating the interpretation.

"Uh, that thing is like, a new sword," she said, trying to explain in a way he would understand. "Made from a metal you've never seen before."

"Ah, new magic," Jonny nodded, as if understanding. "Such things are what nations kill for. This smells like the work of he who wears the 13."

"The Patriot?"

"Yes."

"Tch, why don't you say stuff like normal people?" whined Mindy. "We've got to go find Mark."

Smitty opened the door to the lab.

"Did Mark just come in here?"

"We were just talking about looking for him."

"I wouldn't," warned Smitty. "I don't think the Mark that came in here was Mark."

"These are grim tidings, m'lady. Fix is no match for these demons. He could be consumed like any mortal."

"Well, he's got one trick up his sleeve," Mindy replied, all the while worrying. "I just hope he remembered to put it in his pocket."

While Smitty led Jonny and Mindy out of the room, Gulacy stepped to the side of the room to get a fresh slide for his microscope. A shadowy figure stepped into the room and looking at the globule under Gulacy's examining desk, whispered, "Neck."

The globule shot into Gulacy's neck. He stiffened and fell over. Mark walked into the room with silvery eyes, then morphed into Gulacy.

CHAPTER 32 (Narrator): Hell's Pit Stop

Mark hopped the Speed Line back to Jersey, then took a cab to his parents' place. He managed to sneak through the back door without much of a fuss. His father was playing Pinochle with a group of his friends, while his mother had gone grocery shopping. He said hello through the wall of the utility room.

"Your mother made you dinner. It's in the fridge," his father added.

"Great," thought Mark. "The world is ending and ma packed me a lunch."

Mark ran into the bathroom and looked at his arm under the light. By this time, his arm was pulsating unnaturally and this thing growing inside his hand was almost a foot long. Mark pulled it away from his arm as far as he could. The thing lightly struggled against his grip. Then he took a razorblade and cut it off.

A sharp pain shot through the side of Mark's body, as the severed thing squealed and flopped in the bathroom basin. Mark lost his balance as his arm spasmed. After a few seconds, the pain became a low throbbing and the thing melted down the sink. Mark looked at himself in the mirror, he looked pale and his eyes sunken in.

"Mark?" called his father. "What was that?"

"Nothing!" assured Mark.

"How's his detective thing goin', Mike?" asked one of his friends.

"Pretty good, Mark just wrapped up a case. Mark, what was that case you were on?!"

"Which one, dad?"

"The one you just did, with the fat lady and her robot."

"He was a cyber cop, dad."

"Come out here," insisted dad.

By this time, Mark had put on his other trenchcoat and put his disc player in its pocket. (Mark had no intention on dying without appropriate background music. He popped in a Rage disc.) He downed a few more cold medicine tablets and tried to walk out the back door.

"I don't really have time, dad. I'm right in the middle of something."

"What? Are you okay?"

"Yeah, you don't look so good," added one of his friends.

"I'm-fine-bye."

"Wait, wait, wait, wait," his father gestured, grabbing him by the arm before he could slip away. He guided his son into the neighboring utility room. "I'll be right back, guys. C'mere, Mark."

"C'mon, dad...."

"Now what is it?"

Mark shifted uncomfortably and looked away.

"Nuthin'! I'm in a hurry," said the exasperated P.I.

"Don't tell me *nuthin'*," mocked his father in a voice remarkably similar to his. "Don't be stupid. Are you and Mindy fighting?"

"She still *breathing*, isn't she?"

"Then what? Is this somethin' for the police? Mark, you be careful, your mother and I can't keep putting out money for lawyers. You're thirty years old and —"

"I know, everybody keeps telling me," Mark said through a mouthful of grinding teeth. "I can handle this, okay? This is what I do. I'm not an invalid, I'm just a friggin' loser that lives with his folks."

"Don't be like that," his father said sourly. "I didn't say that. You know your mother and I are proud of you. I know you have your own business and it isn't easy. I'd just wish you'd—Just use your head, okay?"

"All right, all right," relented Mark.

Mark could have told his dad or even everyone in the room. They would've rallied behind him in support, made phone calls and used their resources. But Mark's pride wouldn't have it. This was his mess and going to dad for help was out of the question.

"Rough case, uh... stakeouts and stuff."

"Yeah, sure," added dad unconvincingly.

Sometimes, when Mark talked to his parents, it was like he was eight years old again. He felt inadequate and emasculated in their presence, especially now in front of his dad's friends.

"Take the dinner your mother made."

"But I don't have time —"

"Then take it for later," he insisted.

"Fine!"

Mark took the two Tupperware boxes of food and salad, along with a plastic fork and a packet of dressing, which he put in his pocket. He mumbled a thanks and was out the door. Outside, in front of the Nippon, he felt a twinge a victory. Maybe he still lived at home, but at least he was going to take responsibility for this mess. Do or die, it was his ball to fumble. Then Mindy and everyone else would know what kind of man Mark Mammon was.

On the way back to Philly, he stopped at Castle Burger just to get the toy in the kid's meal. By some miracle, he still had his cell phone and tried dialing Sven at all his haunts. Goda's number was busy. When he reached Goda's precinct, he spotted Mindy coming out of a side door. He skidded to a halt nearby and got out. He was so happy to see her, he didn't even mind missing the last half of his favorite Gravity Kills song on the radio.

"Thank God you're all right! Listen, Min'. This is hard for me to say, but, this whole responsibility thing. You're right, we need to—-"

Mindy spotted a tiny globule of alien protoplasm poking out of Mark's hand. She screamed, causing Mark to whirl around and draw his gun.

"Help! He's here! He's here!" she wailed.

"What? What?!"

Mark couldn't find what she was screaming at and looked around in confusion. Mindy picked up a piece of wood the desk sergeant had been using for a doorstop in the summer and smacked Mark in the back of the head.

"Ow!" Mark squealed in surprised, dropping his gun and stumbling to his knees. "Have you lost your mind?!"

"You bastard, you ate Mark!" screamed Mindy, running back into the station.

"I did not!" insisted Mark, picking up his gun. "Now, what was all that about?"

A few seconds later, a group of heavily armed policemen, led by Goda, came charging out a side door. Mark carefully holstered his gun and put up his hands.

"Don't shoot, it's me! It's me!"

"Just throw down the gun!"

Mark carefully bent down to set the gun on the asphalt, but suddenly, the blob inside his hand shot out and grabbed the piece. It fired just as Mark pulled it away with his left hand.

"Hey! Bad blob!"

"Raymond, throw the thermite!" ordered Goda.

"Thermite? That don't sound good," said Mark, diving into the Nippon.

Mark managed to pull away, just before thermite grenade exploded and burned a two foot crater in the parking asphalt. Mark caught the flash in his rearview mirror and was temporarily blinded.

"Oh! Shouldn't've looked at that."

At the same time, Jonny Plazzz jumped through a second story window and landed on his motorcycle in the parking lot outside. He gunned the engine and was in hot pursuit of Mark.

Inside the police station, Dr. Gulacy made an uncharacteristic visit to the two dispatchers on duty. As he entered the room, he locked the door behind him.

"What do ya say, Pete?" asked the dispatcher that knew him.

"Die, human filth!"

Before the dispatchers could respond, the evil Gulacy's arms had erupted into a fury of limbs that smothered both officers. Gulacy created a third limb, which began destroying the newly remodeled Philadelphia Emergency Response System.

Mark turned the Nippon down Market Street, as Sven launched a bolt of lightning from his sword. It bounced harmlessly off the side of the Reading Terminal.

"Sven!" screamed Mark, as the Asgardian pulled alongside. "It's me! It's me!"

"Demon spawn! You mock the memory of my fallen comrade! You shall——"

Just then, Mark spotted the red light and slammed on his brakes. Sven zoomed into the intersection and was promptly broad-sided by a Center City shuttle bus. The impact sent him flying off the motorcycle and somersaulting into a group of newspaper dispensers in front of the Gallery mall.

Mark could hear police cars just a block away. He took advantage of the commotion to turn down a side street, which would ultimately lead to the highway twelve blocks away.

"Ha! I'm home free!"

Just then, the Nippon sputtered and ran out of gas. Mark had been in such a hurry to get back, he hadn't stopped for gas, but he instantly realized who left him on E.

"Thank *you*, Mindy," he growled to himself, abandoning the car.

Mark ran across the street and into the park on Rittenhouse Square. A crowd had gathered for one of the city's Art events. Mark shoved aside a couple in his way, stumbled over a bump in the sidewalk, then tripped his way into a display of velvet paintings of crying clowns.

"Hey!" objected the artist.

"Sorry," mumbled Mark getting to his feet and noticing the paintings. "No big loss."

Two patrolmen, on duty for park security, spotted the commotion and ran towards Mark. He immediately spotted them and changed direction. He cut around the fountain, jumped over a low hedge and came squarely down on the foot of a mime, who was in the middle of a performance for a group of German tourists.

"Ahhhhhhhhhhhhhhhhhhhhh!" howled the mime in pain.

The tourists promptly took pictures. One of the patrolmen stopped to assess the damage done to the mime, while the second stumbled over the same spot in the sidewalk. Mark looked up just in time to see Sven hurtling toward him, sword raised.

"For Asgaaaaaaaaaaard!"

Mark reached the spin paint table. He unloaded two massive tubes of paint into the spinner, pointed the spinner at Sven as he neared and press the speed of the spinner to "Hi". Red and yellow paint doused the objecting crowd and blinded the son of Thor. He misjudged his landing and crash-landed into the two patrolmen, pushing all three into a clay sculpture. Sven lifted his paint and clay stained face from the mess.

"By the gods! He must be Fix! No other mortal could cause such chaos!"

Mark, completely paint free, skidded to a halt at the corner of the park, just as police cars rounded the corner. He ducked into a nearby office building before anyone saw him.

Inside, he carefully walked the hall watching the police through the windows outside.

"Great," muttered Mark to himself. "Trying to save the world, everyone's trying to kill me and I'm doing it all on spec!"

Just then, Mark's favorite conversationalist, dazed and confused, walked out of the office in front of him.

"Hey, Terry Frenzen...fin, right?!" he asked, way too excited.

"Hello," Mark replied, his face stunned by the coincidence.

"Guess you heard about the Winston merger fiasco, huh?"

Out of the corner of his eye, Mark spotted one of the police officers entering the building. Mark put his arm around dazed and confused and guided him back into the office.

"My God, that's all anyone's talking about!"

"You goin' upstairs?" asked D & C.

"Sure, sure," Mark said enthusiastically. "Upstairs is good."

"You think?" D & C said unsure.

Mark's face was clearly registering panic, but it just didn't sink in with this guy.

"Yes! Immediately! Show me the elevator."

"Wow, I've never seen anyone so anxious to take an corporate assertive training course before," said D & C as Mark pushed him toward another door.

On the floor, Mark and D & C entered during the middle of the instructor's lesson.

"Today, we're going to learn how to deal with an overly-assertive employee," continued the instructor. "I need a volunteer to role-play the employee. You and you in the hat."

"What?" said Mark, who was distracted by watching the windows.

The room's walls were covered three-quarters of the way around with clouded glasses. Mark was anxiously watching them for the police.

"I think he means us," said D & C.

Mark reluctantly stood in the front of the room with D & C, looking nervously from side to side.

"Now, it's all right to be nervous. Is this your first time in front of people?"

"Well, yes," smiled D &C.

"Hmmm? Oh, yeah, whatever."

"Okay, you're the employee," he gestured to Mark. "And you're the manager, I want you to give him an order that —"

Mark spotted the policemen getting off the elevator. They were headed right for one of the doors to the conference room.

"Everybody up against the door!" screamed Mark.

"No, I won't," said D & C triumphantly.

"Good, good," supported the instructor.

Mark pulled out his gun.

"I said get against the fucking door, you knob! NOW!"

A flurry of sheepish employees piled against the door, blocking access to the pursuing authorities. Mark was out the door on the other side and down the hall. As he ran, he shot out the ceiling lights, then kicked over a water cooler into the darkness. Two patrolmen, with no other route to go, slipped in the darkness. By the time they turned the corner, the elevator doors were shutting and the elevator was on its way down.

"He's going back down!"

Mark had pushed the elevator buttons, then ducked into the stairwell and ran up. He reached the roof and jammed the door shut behind him using the handle from a fire extinguisher. He was halfway across the roof before he nearly plowed into chest of one of the most well known (and well endowed) Liberator. She stood with her fists on her waist, waiting for Mark to turn around. Mark turned and his eyes met her breasts.

"Oh, hello, Dorothy."

<u>CHAPTER 33</u> (Mark): Meet the Liberators

Yeah, I know. Superheroes. Those of you who don't live in Philadelphia probably don't even believe in them. (Hell, I know people who meet them all the time and they still don't believe it.) Sven and I met when he was still part of the team. (He was accused of murdering rookie superguy, Atomic Dom.)

Needless to say, yours truly and the Stuff saved the day. The history of the Liberators is a long and interesting one, but I really don't have time for that, so here are the highlights:

The original group was formed during the Revolutionary War as part of an elite, underground fighting force of patriots. It was then disbanded and reformed after the war to combat rampant crime in post-war America. The only thing anyone seems to know about the first two teams is that one of the members was a shadowy figure known as Patriot 13.

Over the next two hundred years or so, the Liberators reformed and disbanded, often during times of war. One of the members was always Patriot 13. (Whether or not this is the same Patriot 13 is unknown, but the other members were usually different.)

During the Twenties', the group earned an infamous reputation by putting down labor strikes for large companies. This was later revealed to be a corporate-backed group of thugs paid by the same companies and organized crime. Sometime later, perhaps in response to the desecration of the name, the 1920's Liberator team was systematically murdered by a mysterious avenger named, (you guessed it) Patriot 13.

In the late Thirties', the group reformed again and made a name for itself fighting crime. A ruthless Philadelphia Assistant D.A. made a name for himself branding the Liberators as outlaws and even prosecuting several of the members. But by the time World War Two rolled around, public support of the Liberators was back on the rise.

This is the group of Liberators everyone knows. The ones with the superpowers and the ones that saved FDR from a Nazi assassination plot. And, although they were not officially backed by the government, the laws prohibiting vigilantism, especially in Philadelphia were greatly relaxed.

As the late Forties'-early Fifties' rolled around, the Liberators became more and more a Philadelphia tradition. Members were often asked to speak at schools and lead parades, despite the fact that even after all these years, no one knew the real identity of these people. But public support was so strong, the Liberators weren't even subpoenaed during the McCarthy hearings. Their heroism inspired the locals to throw a parade and their sometimes outlandish costumes were incorporated into it. Local laws prohibited the gatherings early on, so the parades were kept "mum" until the last minute. Thus, the Mummers' Parades were born.

By the late fifties, most of the famous members had retired and the group was pretty much down to public appearances. However, a new, younger generation of superhero came up the pike. A rift developed between the old and new heroes.

During the late Sixties', the rift blossomed into all out warfare. Public opinion split right down the middle and it pretty much drove the group underground again. When the dust settled, sometime in the mid-seventies', the group's new leader, had reinvented superheroes.

Sponsored by a millionaire philanthropist, he built the Liberators a public headquarters, then set it up as a non-profit organization. The PR was too good to pass up and companies rushed to sponsor them. Sometime later, the group's members were officially deputized by local authorities.

During the Eighties', the group was franchised to other cities. Superheroes were marketed as a new type of celebrity. Unfortunately, even though all this money and attention had saved the Liberators from oblivion, it ultimately doomed it.

The superheroes who joined became instant celebrities and soon found out they could make more money by going private. At the same time, the group was hit with a series of devastating lawsuits from criminal suspects and their lawyers, who challenged the Liberators' jurisdiction.

Ultimately, to save the team, the group was officially made a branch of law enforcement in 1988. At first, the changes were subtle, but slowly but surely, a new regime of Liberator crept in. Members were required to undergo background checks and take training. Red uniforms were issued and rules of engagement were set. Some of the heroes either quit in protest, others were forced to retire and a handful even went to jail for continuing unsanctioned crime fighting.

Sven quit shortly after the Vine Street incident, in which several of the locals, mostly black, were attacked by a racist Liberator. For weeks, public opinion turned way ugly and to this day, I don't think it's ever recovered.

I sure as hell don't trust 'em. They're just like any other government arm, full of people who couldn't hack it anywhere else. I mean, why would anyone in this day and age with godly powers work for the U.S. government? They even screw *themselves*! What they got left on the team these days are FBI rejects, superhumans on super power trips and a few competent members of the Armed Forces who weren't killed by the secret medical experiments only seen by Mulder and Scully. Dorothy's one of them, Codename: Ms. Maser. A female, marine, cyborg with a bitchin' attitude and a bod to match. I don't know why Sven ever broke up with her.

"Fix," she growled, grabbing me by the lapels and pulling my eyes away from her tremendous tatas. "Why am I not surprised?"

"Well, because your cybernetic senses can hear a mouse take a pee a mile away in high winds," I quipped.

"For God's sake commander!" squealed her lackey, Peter. "He's infected!"

Peter was a squirmy little guy, barely twenty, with a wisp of a hairline and eyes the size of silver dollars. A genetic abnormality in his genes gave him the ability to think at twice the speed of a normal human, thereby doubling his reflexes and decreasing his reaction time, while increasing his senses. But, his eyes, ears and nose grew to freak-like sizes and even though he could think twice as fast, it didn't make him any smarter.

He and the rest of the group were wearing those dorky, red Liberator uniforms with blue and white trim that Dorothy is so proud of. Peter's code name was clearly stitched over his right pocket: Neuron Pete.

I might've been able to talk ol' NP into calming down, but Dorothy was backed by this edgy Latino hermaphrodite code named, Witch Juan. I think he/she had some kind of secret, Aztec magic powers. Word was Juan only got on the team, because Dorothy needed to fill some kind of government minority quota.

Dorothy tended to use the biggest fuck-ups whenever she went on a mission, since that made it easier to keep Liberator PR disasters to a minimum. I guess that's why she had Mr. Scrotum—I mean, Mr. Quantum—Scott with her.

"Drop him, commander!" suggested Scott. "I'll fry his ass before it hits the ground!"

"Calm down, Liberator," she instructed. "I can assure you, the only thing I'm in danger of is Fix copping a feel. And I better not even be in danger of that."

"Can't feel anything in those thick uniforms anyway. So, beat any good civilians recently?"

"No, but I'm itching to start," she growled, shoving me to the ground.

"Yeah, well, in case you don't know it, the friggin' world's about to end. I believe it's *your* job to do something about it?" I said, as sarcastically as possible. "We got aliens runnin' around, absorbing stupid people, ruining perfectly good trenchcoats—-"

"Wait a minute," she suspiciously. "How do you know about the aliens?"

"Oh, I don't know, *Einstein*," I said, holding up my hand, which was leaking of the strange goo. "I may have bumped into one!"

"You see!" squeaked Pete. "I told you!"

"I sense a great pain in him," added Juan, putting his hand to his forehead dramatically.

"I'll give him a pain," offered Scott, immediately stepping forward, but was stopped by Dorothy.

"There's no time. We have to get him back to headquarters before—-"

Finally, the police, led by Goda and Sven, burst onto the roof. Dorothy gnashed her teeth, made a fist and punched herself in the thigh.

"Dammit," she muttered.

"Dorothy!" beamed Sven. "Fix is not himself, he —"

"I know," she relented. "I know exactly what's wrong with him and what's going on. You'll all have to be debriefed back at headquarters. This is a matter of national security."

"But," I interrupted. "Their leader, Gornon is killing people. He —"

"He is working with us," explained Dorothy. "He's not trying to kill us; he may be the only person who can save us."

<u>CHAPTER 34</u> (Narrator): 13 Ways to Die

Mark was escorted to a waiting Liberator vehicle on the ground floor. Dorothy took charge of Goda's men, much to his annoyance, and kept them in a constant circle, but at a constant distance, from the infected P.I. Mark felt like he was being transported like a walking time bomb. Everyone seemed to be afraid he'd go off. Even Jonny.

"I don't like this, Sven," he whispered to the Asgardian. "Everything's going topsy-turvy. I don't know who to trust."

"Be brave, friend Fix. Dorothy's wizards are the best in the Realm."

"This is Philadelphia, we kicked the king's ass two hundred and twenty years ago. It's not a *Realm!*"

"You are in a sour mood," said Sven, hurt, as he turned his nose away.

Mark looked around for someone else to vent his frustration on and picked Goda.

"What are you lookin' at?" he sneered.

"Throw the thermite," mocked Mark. "You putz. The Mangas nearly tore me a new asshole thanks to you!"

"What are you talking about? The Mangas have been in lock up since you went berserk, *genius!*"

"I don't think so, *Barney Fife*. All I've been doin' for the last six hours is gettin' my ass handed to me and most of the guys know how to pronounce sasi — shasi — sa —"

"Sashimi?"

"Sashimi, thank you. Did someone at least tie down Smitty?"

"Yeah, and you might be interested to know what we found."

"Yeah?"

"I didn't say I was gonna tell you."

"Look, either start talkin' about Smitty or get me to a sushi bar, I'm starvin' here!"

Goda quickly filled Mark in on the briefing, just as Mark prepared to step into the waiting van. All around the area, a normal security team that worked with the Liberators helped disperse the crowd. Just then, Mindy's cab skidded to a halt and she ran to the edge of the crowd. Mark immediately spotted her.

"Mark?" she called sheepishly.

"Oh, hello!" Mark said sarcastically as possible. "Would you like to hit me with a

Stop sign now?!"

"Well," Mindy stammered on the verge of fake tears. "They told me you were eaten and—They said you were evil, but—Your hand was melting!"

"I'll melt you!"

Mark tried to lunge at her, but was immediately stopped by the cops and Goda. The goo shot out of Mark's hand and brushed against Goda's face.

"Get her in a car!" Dorothy ordered. "You better get in the van with Fix."

"Me?!" objected Goda. "You picked him up!"

"I didn't touch him with bare skin. The infection just rubbed against your face. It's just a precaution," she assured.

Inside the dark van, Goda and Mark felt their way to parallel stretchers on either side of the vehicle. Goda pushed Mark away from him.

"Don't touch me again, moron!" snapped Goda, nerves frayed.

"You're shoving me, butt munch! You think I'm enjoying this?"

"Just stay to your side, as far as I'm concerned, you're one o' them! If you hadn't delayed us in the squad room..."

"What the Hell are you talking about? I didn't even get inside the building!" spewed Mark, beside himself.

"Just lie back and shut up."

Outside the van, Sven and Dorothy had one of their long string of bittersweet reunions.

"Hello, Sven," she greeted at once being both distant and intimate. "How's the salon?"

"Mr. Vidal is quaking in his boots!" smiled Sven, following her into a waiting car.

Dorothy's driver was a grey-skinned, Liberator cadet, with pock-marked, stone-like skin and no nose.

"Back to HQ, Doug," she instructed.

"Yes, ma'am," replied the rock boy.

"T'is is like old times!" boomed Sven. "What a shame we haven't time for a drink and a song."

"I might take you up on that later," Dorothy replied coyly. "I'm glad you're back, Sven."

"Not back, exactly, although you know I'm always ready for a battle. Now, about, Fix..."

"Fix," scoffed Dorothy, disgusted at the very mention. "I wish you wouldn't get involved with that scumbag."

"Mind your words, woman. He is my friend."

"Yeah, well he's in over his head again. You both are."

"The Son of Thor is ready to stand fast! What manner of problem plagues us?"

"Keep this between us, but the Liberators have been put on Level 6 Alert."

"Loki's lapels!" gasped Sven.

"The president himself reactivated all able-bodied Liberators, even the reservists. You probably got the message on your machine."

"So the threat isn't just to the City of Brothers or even the United States, but...."

"The Earth. The whole enchilada. We're being invaded."

Back in the van...

"Did you ever stop and think that, had you listened to me in the first place, you wouldn't be in this mess?!" whined Mark.

"Did you ever stop and think, that if you didn't act like such a goofball, I might've listened to ya?" snapped Goda.

"Goofball?!" Mark seethed. "That's it. Hold me back."

Just then, restraints popped up from the stretchers, holding Goda and Mark fast.

"I was only kidding."

"I didn't do it!"

A dim bulb on the ceiling of the van lit the chamber and a masked figure with a circle of 13 stars leaned forward.

"Ahhh!" screamed Mark in surprise. "It's Betsy Ross!"

"You *imbecile*," the Patriot's voice rumbled. "This entire country hangs by a thread thanks to you. Do you have any idea what's at stake? The cost of your bumbling?!"

"Well, I usually charge $100 an hour, but I'll run a special for you."

"Hey, I'm on your side," Goda pitched to the Patriot. "What's all this—"

The Patriot pushed a button and a metal restraint pressed down over Goda's mouth.

"Thanks," quipped Mark. "He was driving me *crazy*. Can I go home now?"

Irritated, but composed, the Patriot ignored Mark and tapped on the wall of the van, signaling the driver to begin moving.

"You're infected, Fix and I don't see any sign of your *power* reversing that effect," noted the Patriot, suppressing a smile.

"Oh, my God!" thought Mark. "He knows!"

"Perhaps you'd like to use what little time you have to tell me what you know."

"I'm sure we have *plenty* of time for that. How about you tell me why the U.S. government would cut a deal with a monster like Gornon?"

"Dorothy already told you, he's here to save us. Unfortunately, for you, you have been infected with a tiny Kaltherian microbe, which can only be stopped by Gornon's unique genetic engineering capabilities."

"Yeah, I don't suppose he's in the mood to do me any favors. I don't suppose you're going to tell me why he and his boys have been hacking up the locals? Or why they stashed some kind of rocket fuel in a medical supply warehouse?"

"No."

There was an awkward silence. Mark couldn't see the Patriot's face, so he wasn't sure if he was finished talking.

"And now?" asked Mark.

"And now, Mr. Fix. You die."

<u>CHAPTER 35</u> (Narrator): Meet the Maine

The Maine Building sat like a short, squat, giant Rubik's cube, on the corner of Eighth and Arch Streets. It had its own underground parking garage, which never seemed to fill. Mark had long ago surmised the enigma of its architecture, but decided that exploring further wasn't worth the aggravation. Too many powerful people (both physically and politically) wanted the Maine to be kept a secret.

It's ominous presence alone, kept most of the locals away. The steel and glass were so dark, you could miss the front door several times before finding it. Each group of employees was departmentalized and each floor had its own security. Several secret government projects could be run out of the Maine, sometimes running counter to the others, without the other group knowing. Patriot 13 was one of five men on the planet that could access almost any floor and even he couldn't access them all. If it was secret, it was probably in the Maine.

Mark was so exhausted, as he lay back on the stretcher, he dozed off. His dreams were a fitful nightmare of slaughter and carnage, mixed with Kaltherian genetics. He stood atop the Tally Ho arcade in the early morning. A mist descending on the parking lot below. As he reached the edge of the roof, the mist cleared. Hundreds—Thousands of people were walking toward him, giggling, calling to him and asking for beer.

And they all looked like Smitty.

"Jeez!" Mark exclaimed, waking with a start.

He was sitting in a sterile cell, with smooth, off-white, concave walls. On one side, there was a stainless steel door and on the other, a large window looking out over a chamber. While he slept, the goo had crept up his arm and towards his face. Totally skeeved, Mark brushed the goo back in a vain attempt to get it off.

The room below looked like a casting call for the super friends. Dozens of men and women, all with powers and abilities far beyond those of mortal men, milled around what looked like a briefing room full of security monitors. They ranged from a ten-foot-tall, hairless blue giant to a six-inch-tall blonde, who flitted around the room on her tiny jetpack. On one side of the room, Witch Juan chatted casually with a man covered from head to toe in purple flame, while standing by a support pillar, an agitated Scott Quantum and Sven sipped coffee from Styrofoam cups. Liberators from Washington, New York,

Atlanta, Orlando, and Chicago, mixed with other teams, as their uniforms blurred into a sea of red.

In a secure waiting room nearby, a group of the police officers were patiently sitting at a table, eating donuts, while Mindy, bored to tears, flipped through a copy of News Weekly, which featured the Liberators cover story from last March.

"Fix!" hissed Goda from the next cell.

Out of the corner of his eye, through the reflection, Mark could barely make out Goda. He was in an identical cell next to him.

"How long have they been at this?" asked Mark.

"About an hour, I don't think they can see us up here. How's the hand?"

"Disgusting," replied Mark, noting Goda's friendlier attitude. "Look, I'm really sorry if I infected you. I shouldn't have lunged for Mindy."

"It's okay. Even I wanted to strangle Tina a few times."

"Who's that? Your wife?"

"Yeah, thanks for askin'."

"Oh, jeez, now he's gonna lay a guilt trip on me. Look, I don't know about you, but I don't think they have us in here just to play Yahtzee."

"Yeah, so?"

"So, I think this thing I'm infected with is Gornon."

"What?"

"It all makes sense. Smitty was the only survivor on the ship. Gornon engineered the crew so they'd be able to recreate themselves if they split."

"And that's what they did, right?"

"Yeah, but Smitty was all mixed up with John Schmidt's DNA. Gornon couldn't have accounted for that. It must've made all the new Kaltherians weaker. I saw one melting, he said something about cellular degeneration."

"So they need a human protein to stabilize their cellular structure," Goda put together.

Mark looked back at him, a little surprised.

"I told you," Goda said embarrassed. "I'm a trekkie. But why'd they'd keep hacking up everybody?"

"Because they can't use just anyone, they have to use someone with comparable DNA. They used the medical tests as a front to find humans with the right genes. The livers must've been part of the test. That also explains why they always look like football players, they can only mimic what Smitty's done."

"But at City Hall, they mimicked those old people."

"That's because those two Kaltherians must've already stabilized."

"So how does Victor tie in?"

"Victor stuck me with this needle in my infected hand. Maybe the Kaltherians tainted a shipment of Toxic Ito's drugs; they said their dealers had been hit with a plague. And the Patriot called it a Kaltherian microbe. It could lay dormant in say, heroin, until it was injected."

"Yeah and the microbe eats up the junkie from the inside out."

"Victor's DNA must've been a match and mine is obviously not. Oh, my God! So in a way, Victor really was the killer! Damn, I'm smooth."

Goda looked down into the briefing room. The Patriot, escorted by two nondescript-looking men in suits and sunglasses, entered and gestured for everyone to gather around the bank of monitors.

"Hey, Cap'n Smoothie, get a load of this."

"Citizens, Liberators, members of law enforcement," began the Patriot. "We gather today to avert the greatest crisis this country has ever known."

The Patriot dimmed the lights and gestured to a monitor which held the appropriate graphics to demonstrate the situation.

"As of this moment, a fleet of ten thousand alien vessels, part of an organization known as the Imperial Conquistadors, waits in suspended animation, just beyond our asteroid belt."

"Dear Jesus," gasped Goda.

"My covert team has been working with a secret group of alien defectors. In exchange for political asylum, they have given us the information to attack the fleet while it still sleeps and the technology to destroy it."

On cue, the two men on either side of the Patriot unsheathed two tiny, compact devices that resembled pieces of silver driftwood. They aimed the devices at an empty table. A tiny, bright blue beam shot forth, freezing the table and then shattering it into tiny ice-like fragments. A murmur of surprise and awe rippled through the Liberator ranks.

Mark looked at Dorothy, gauging her reaction. She was probably the only other person that hated the Patriot more than Mark did, yet she stood quietly and let him take over her whole operation. Mark detected only a faint whisper of frustration in her, as she shifted her weight anxiously.

He spotted Smitty, standing in a corner by himself, apparently forgotten by the rest of the room. He looked bored and depressed, having resigned himself to the fact that all his friends were as good as dead. He was thinking about slipping away, so he wouldn't have to watch it all in person.

Upstairs, while the weight of the world hung in the balance, Mindy read an interesting article about shellfish.

"Using our newly acquired technology," continued the Patriot, turning on the lights in the adjoining hangar. "We have constructed four space-faring vessels, capable of traversing the distance to the asteroid belt in less than a week. Ms. Maser will lead the attack teams on the flagship, New York team will take ship two, Washington and Atlanta, ship 3 and Chicago and the others, ship 4, while I coordinate attack from our base here."

"How convenient," muttered Mark.

"Holy shit!" said Goda in amazement. "They got space ships down here?"

"Our experts calculate that you will be able to destroy or disable seventy-three percent of the vessels before the fleet's onboard computers can wake up their crews. We believe that faced with such devastating losses, the Conquistadors will retreat. In the event that they continue their attack..."

"Hey! Hey!" screamed Mark, pounding on the window of his cell.

The Patriot hesitated and a few of the Liberators looked up in Mark's direction.

"Our plan is to deploy a series of advance warning satellites, which will —"

Mark continued to pound and scream. The goo leaking out of his hand formed several dozen little fists and joined in on the tapping. Although Mark's voice wasn't audible, the acoustics of the room magnified the pounding, until the Patriot could no longer continue.

"Hey! Heeeeeeeeeeeeeeeeey!!!"

"But before I continue with the plan which may very well save this country, if not the planet, I believe Mr. Fix has something to say," the Patriot gritted between his teeth.

Pressing a button, the glass on Mark and Goda's cell went from tinted to clear and all eyes turned toward Mark.

"YOU DON'T EVEN —!"

Mark's voice boomed across the room, magnified by the intercom in his cell. The speakers cracked and feedback assaulted everyone's ears. The Patriot turned the volume down.

"We can hear you now," he explained.

"Oh," said Mark. "Um, ahem, what I was, uh, saying," he continued, now nervous with all eyes upon him. "How do you know there are ten thousand ships up there?"

"The evidence we have clearly shows a number of metallic objects within the asteroid belt."

"Aren't asteroids made out of metal?" asked Goda.

"Yeah!" agreed Mark.

"We've been assured they are not," added the Patriot icily. "Now, the plan —"

"Who assured you?" interrupted Dorothy, suddenly very interested.

"We don't have time for this," the Patriot assured.

"Who?" she repeated patiently.

"Why don't you ask the man himself?" replied 13, activating a monitor.

The screen surged to life. It showed the inside of some kind of bridge, like that of a battleship. Victor directed what looked like Miami's Mort Domino and The Fridge, to monitoring stations thirteen and seventy-two feet away. To his left, Washington's star running back pressed a lighted sensitive display, which controlled the ship's altitude, while the Great Brad Jakes sat in the navigation seat, plotting the ship's next flight path every thirty-two minutes. A cheerleader dressed in a scanty blue and orange uniform, assisted Cleveland's mascot in repairing some computer circuits. Victor, noticed he was being watched; acknowledged the camera with a nod.

"Ah, the humans," he said to his crew. "We haven't much time. Has your group been briefed?"

"Partly," said the Patriot. "This is Gornon Fthal, a Commander in the Kaltherian advanced infantry unit."

"He's a murderer!" shouted Goda.

"Yeah, what about that *commander*?" asked Mark.

Gornon/Victor shot a surprised, angry glance at the P.I. as if to say, "You?!". Then composed himself and continued.

"Your half robot is right. We did kill to survive, as did some of you," his eyes drifted toward Smitty, who looked away in shame in embarrassment. "But that unpleasantness is over, we have no more need to harm any of you."

"Yeah, right," muttered Goda.

"We were originally sent to your planet to infiltrate your armies and cause dissent. When our operatives were secure in their positions, we were to signal the rest of the fleet to attack. Unfortunately, our craft was sabotaged by the ship's philosopher, Rojbor."

"Smitty," yelled Mark across the room. "Is that true?"

"I-I-I don't remember," stammered the alien.

"The rest of us were killed and only Rojbor survived. It was only recently that —"

Mark felt another sharp pain shoot down his arm. Gornon/Victor swooned, as if getting lightheaded. A surprised expression crossed his face for a second, then disappeared.

"Excuse me. Recently, we were revived by a genetic program encoded in Rojbor's DNA."

"And now you want to take over," added Mark.

"If only we could," admitted Gornon/Victor. "Shortly before the crash, my second-in-command, Urgo..."

Gornon/Victor gestured toward someone in the background who looked amazingly like Willy Rapp of the '92 Philadelphia defensive line. Willy bowed in acknowledgement.

"...decoded a secret message from the invading flagship. The invasion of your world had been canceled because its resources were not profitable enough."

"Then what's the problem?" asked Dorothy.

"The High Commander ordered that your planet be destroyed from space, with us still on the surface. We bartered our information and technology in exchange for resources to build our own ship."

"Then why did you ask Smitty to go with you?" asked Goda. "You said he would die with the filthy humans."

"Because even though we've given you our technology, you can't possibly stand up to the might of the fleet. That's why we're leaving."

"Like rats on a sinking ship," muttered Sven.

"Precisely," smiled Gornon/Victor.

This seemed to convince the assembled multitude. Sure Gornon was a bad guy, he admitted it. But it all made sense to everyone present. A murmur bounced around the room like a shockwave.

"Oh, very neat," Mark said disbelievingly. "You're just like VH's management, you've got a nice little excuse for everything, don't you? You want to know what I think?! You're full of shit, Victor! You're just trying to get the Liberators out of the way, so you can blow us out of the water!"

Another murmur shook the crowd.

"Do what you will, humans," Gornon/Victor dismissed. "We're leaving and if ten thousand Imperial warships hanging over your heads don't bother you, well, I could give a rat's ass!"

And with that, Gornon/Victor abruptly signed off.

"Ms. Maser," said a hopeful, young superhero, who looked to be made entirely out of chrome. "What do you think?"

Dorothy put her hand to her chin thoughtfully. Her shoulders sank as if the weight of the world pushed them down.

"Don't believe 'em, Dorothy! He —"

The Patriot dimmed Mark's cell. Dorothy lifted up her head.

"Let's kick some alien ass!"

The Liberators cheered, caught up in the heady prelude to war.

"No! NO!" insisted Mark, pounding on the glass again.

But it was no use, caught up in the moment, the Patriot and Maser began organizing the world's most powerful beings into a four part assault team, against an overwhelming enemy. It was a textbook superhero crisis.

"You stupid superheroes! Damn, he's fed right into their egos!" ranted Mark, then muttered to himself. "Stupid Independence Day movie."

The door to Goda's cell opened. Captain McLane had come to bail out his own.

"Cap! Good to see ya."

"C'mon, Tommy," he said. "You've been given a clean bill of health."

"Goda! Tell him!" Mark shouted desperately. "Tell him about the set up!"

"Set up?" asked McLane innocently.

"C'mon, Fix," Goda said reluctantly. "They admitted the murders. Why would they bother to go through all the motions if they were gonna invade?"

"Because they need the Liberators out of the way! One of Gornon's boys said he'd be runnin' the planet by the end of the week and it all has to do with a *stadium*. Isn't there a game tonight at the Vet? Oh, my God! Goda, you gotta tell 'em!"

"C'mon, Tommy," said McLane. "We've got a lot of work to do."

"I'll talk to 'em," Goda assured Mark.

"Talk?! You gotta stop 'em! Goda!"

As Mark pounded on the door of his cell in vain, McLane and Goda headed upstairs to the lobby. Downstairs in the hangars, the last hope for America and Earth; assembled to board the waiting ships. Each ship was roughly bus shaped, covered with the same heat-resistant tiles that protect the space shuttles. The ships were about sixty feet long, with alien propulsion systems in the back, which would lift them into the air with about as much noise as a hair dryer. There was also a side door just wide enough for two people to enter at a time.

Dorothy was already in the flagship, putting her Marine pilot skills to use. The Liberators, all packed like sardines, donned specially outfitted space suits and filed into the ships. Dorothy's co-pilot was a genetically engineered half-man, half-wasp, who went by the codename: Stinger, although mostly everyone just called him Buzz.

"Can this thing really leave the Earth's atmosphere?" she asked to reassure herself.

"It did in all the test runs. We went to the moon and back on Thursday."

"Gnarly," she added, impressed.

In ship two, Sven sat behind the pilots and led the ship in a Viking victory song, which boomed throughout the hangar and bolstered the spirits of all.

Back in his cell, Mark paced around, trying to think of a way out. He noticed that the goo leaking out of his hand would sometimes mimic what his real hand was doing. He willed it to leak under the door, then tried to form a hand to open the cell from the outside. The tiny little hands just didn't have enough mass to move the handle. Mark began to feel a little faint and retracted the goo back, leaving some of it behind.

There was a steel mirror and sink in the cell and Mark splashed water in his face in an effort to clear his head. He coughed and hacked up what he thought was phlegm, but it quickly raced down the drain on a power all its own. Mark looked into the mirror. The goo was leaking out of his nose, it too went back into his head with a power all its own.

"Oh, man. I don't think my HMO's gonna cover this."

Mark heard an odd, kind of squishing sound. He turned around to see Smitty slide himself under the door and reform in front of Mark.

"Mark —"

"Smitty, thank God! Open the door and get me out, we don't have much time."

"I can't, you could infect everybody."

"You know about this stuff, you know a cure right?"

"Mark, whatever would cure you would also kill you. I-I'm sorry. It doesn't matter anyway, we're all dead."

Mark grabbed Smitty by the shoulders and threw him up against the side of the cell.

"Stop saying that! Look, you want to live your life like a miserable fuck, go ahead! But don't assume that everyone else is giving up! You're the only one that can help, you've got to get Mindy out of here and stop the Liberators from leaving."

"I-I can't..."

"Why?!"

"Because, I can't do that as me. I mean, I've won Super Bowls, I've been a coach, a player, a sports caster—I was even a mascot."

"So what?"

"I was always another person, it didn't matter if I won or not, I was just a substitute. This—I can't take the responsibility."

"Smitty," said Mark, deadly serious. "Drunk Boy, listen. I never asked you for anything—Well, except that one time you set me up with the stripper."

"Wasn't she sweet?"

"Yeah," remembered Mark, momentarily distracted. "But, this is different. I'm gonna be dead soon, but if our friendship means anything, you'll get Mindy out of here. For me. And if this planet means anything, you'll do something to get them to stop leaving."

Smitty looked down at his feet, mustering whatever determination was left after all these years of being a spineless drunk. If Kaltherians could sweat, he would've been doing it in buckets.

"Okay," Smitty replied uneasily, as if suddenly lucid for the first time. "Wait here."

"No! Get me out of here first!" insisted Mark.

Goda had followed McLane upstairs to the Maine's lobby. Ironically, the room was run by one, very normal, petite human secretary named Stacey, who checked visitors in and out with the sort of curt efficiency they perfected in Nazi Germany. A metallic archway overlooked the whole room. Despite its decorative look, it was actually a state of the art scanning device that could detect anything from a gun to mutant DNA. A pair of armed security guards monitored the security cameras for the entrance.

"Hey, Cap, I'm surprised they let you in here," said Goda. "This being all hush-hush."

"Being a cybercop does have its advantages, speaking of which—I got called away during most of the commotion, where's the rest of the squad?"

"Well, uh, Gene's downstairs trying to get some official statement for this mess. The rest are either back at the precinct or on the street lookin' for us, I guess."

"You mean, they don't know where you are?"

"No."

"Oh," said McLane thoughtfully. "Good."

McLane/Urgo burst open on one side, shooting a flurry of alien tentacles at the surprised cybercop. Goda landed roughly against a wall of framed plaques, given to the Liberators over the years for their service to Philadelphia. On the other side of the wall, Mindy looked up from her magazine.

One of the guards, reached for his gun, but the second guard, who looked amazingly like "Nasty" Greg James, slammed his head against a video monitor, while shooting a limb seventy-five feet across the lobby, catching Stacey's arm, before she could hit the alarm button. It was all over in a matter of seconds.

"Bring the female here," instructed McLane/Urgo. "Open the front doors."

Stacey tried to use her martial arts training to flip Nasty Greg across the room, but as soon as she pulled on his arm, it elongated, like a giant Stretch Armstrong. She also kicked McLane/Urgo in the chest, much to his disgust.

"Don't let her touch me!" he squealed. "Open the doors, human!"

"B-b-but they're already unlocked," replied the terrified Stacey.

"Not that one, the service door. The one with the wide doorway."

Stacey gestured to the appropriate button and McLane/Urgo pushed it. The doors unclasped and swung open. Outside, silhouetted by the streetlights, four, immensely obese people, hobbled toward the entrance. McLane/Urgo chuckled with perverse delight, while poor Stacey screamed her lungs out.

Downstairs, the Patriot sat in a web of monitors and computers that made the Pentagon's system look like a Fisher Price playset. Keystone and Mass each monitored their own stations.

"Status on flag ship," began the Patriot. "Are we a go?"

"Roger that 13," replied Dorothy over her headset.

"Ships two, three and four?"

"All systems go, sir," replied Keystone.

"Prepare to seal the doors in thirty seconds. Flag ship—"

"Sir," interrupted Mass.

"Standby, flag ship. What is it, agent?"

"We've got an authorized use of a security door near the hangars," reported Mass. "Security codes identify him as a Liberator, codename: Weather Man."

"Winston," the Patriot said aloud, remembering him from the old days. "Just what this mission needs, bad jokes about humidity."

"Should I send a detail, sir?"

"We don't have time, just let the old geezer ride along," the Patriot relented, annoyed at the delay in his finest hour. "Flag ship, stand by. Agent Keystone, open the roof while we're waiting."

The center of the Maine was thought to be the most top secret portion of the building. The doors that led to its center were actually fake and led to nowhere. The entire center of the Maine was one big hidden shaft, with a hydraulic elevator, capable of lifting aircraft to the roof. Although these new spaceships were too big for the elevator, they could be launched from the base of the shaft so effortlessly, they could leave the building without leaving a scratch on it. And the only people who would see the ships leave, would be the homeless in Franklin Park that happened to be looking in the direction of the Maine when they lifted off.

Slowly the lid of the shaft, which also doubled as a helipad, opened. Sven looked up through the shaft and at the stars with a worried look on his face. The Liberator sitting next to him, was one of the old school heroes. Codename: Sea Hawk, his uniform was dotted with the patterns of orange and green fish and other ocean wildlife. His powers were mostly aquatic, but he was taken along anyway.

"What's wrong, big guy?" he asked Sven.

"Outer space," he muttered to himself. "I'd rather face a thousand frost giants armed with nothing but my styling comb!"

"Hey, you know how many fish there are in space?" he replied, a little insulted. "How do you think *I* feel?"

Suddenly, the lights of the hangar when out, the roof doors stopped moving and power in the whole building went out.

"Give me back up! Give me back up!" shouted the Patriot to his men.

"All right, Drunk Boy," Mark smiled to himself.

"Flag ship to 13," said Dorothy. "What's the problem out there?"

"Stand by, Flag ship."

"Stand by *now*?" Dorothy said to Buzz in disbelief.

Too frustrated to sit still, Scott got up and walked to the open side door. Dorothy immediately spotted him.

"Liberator, sit down!" she ordered.

"*I'll* find out what's goin' on here," insisted Scott.

Quantum stormed out of the ship in a huff. Several of the Liberators moved to stop him, but Dorothy gestured for them to let him go.

"Forget it," she said exasperated. "Maybe we can do this mission in peace, now."

As Scott exited the hangar, four fat men were just rounding the corner. Mark recognized Quantum the second he walked across the room.

"Hey, Scott! Scott!"

"I'm busy!" he snapped.

"Yeah, I'm busy too," taunted Mark. "Busy with *Glor-ee-ah.*"

Quantum stopped in his tracks. Mark made a thrusting motion with his pelvis.

"Maybe I'll get busy with her, while you're off fightin' the Martians. Uh, uh!"

"That's it! You're dead meat, Fix!"

The Patriot, spotting the commotion from across the room, gestured to his men.

"Put a man on him!"

Scott easily threw Keystone aside, lifted into the air, pointed his hands together and shot a red beam of energy toward Mark. It melted the window, then shot past him and melted a hole in the wall of the cell.

Back in the flagship, Dorothy was listening to the whole embarrassing incident on her headset. She put her hand to her forehead, took off the headset and rubbed her temples.

"I think he's wound a little too tight for this work," suggested Buzz.

"You think?" Dorothy replied sarcastically.

Just then, the Weather Man, looking about three-hundred pounds heavier, waddled into the doorway of the ship. A Liberator with an oversized brain immediately recognized him.

"Hey, Winston. You made it!"

At the same time, on the other three ships, an obese Japanese thug, a four-hundred-pound Jamaican and a three-hundred and fifty-pound amateur skier wrapped in bandages waddled to the doorways of the ships, much to the confusion of the passengers therein.

"Eye of Odin!" exclaimed Sven. "He'll sink the ship!"

"Winston?" Dorothy said, incredulous, back on the flagship.

"Dor-o-thy," he moaned with great effort. "...run."

Somewhere on the opposite end of the hangar, McLane/Urgo took a blue and gold disc out of his pocket and pressed the button. A high, sustained pitched, filled the hangar. Simultaneously, all four of the obese men began to expand even more. Dorothy's eyes widened in fright.

"Look out!"

Almost simultaneously, the fat men exploded, spreading a semi-transparent goo all over the inside of the ship. The first few rows of Liberators were completed covered and began to be consumed almost immediately. Pandemonium ensued, as the remaining Liberators either panicked or blundered their way into certain death.

Back in the cell, Scott was so furious, he was fighting Mark with his bare hands. Although his powers were considerable, his strength was only that of a normal man. Unused to scuffling, he was rolling around on the floor of the cell, trying to get a grip on the detective's throat.

"Okay, okay," relented Mark, trying to breathe through his hands. "You're the mack-daddy superhero, with the fattest powers and the bulge to match."

"Fuckin' A!" replied Scott, seemingly satisfied, for the moment, with the bizarre apology.

Suddenly, a raucous, deep laughed echoed through the room below and both Mark and Scott turned to see where it came from. McLane/Urgo and Nasty Greg strutted into the room, while the Patriot and his two agents scrambled to help the trapped Liberators.

"Well, Mr. 13," laughed McLane/Urgo. "I just stopped by to thank you, on behalf of Gornon."

"Acquire target, immediately," he responded calmly.

Agents Keystone and Mass took up positions on either side of the Patriot, drawing their new weapons. The Patriot himself drew forth several tiny blue discs, each one with a white star.

"Target acquired," Mass and Keystone said simultaneously.

McLane/Urgo laughed sinisterly, as the two agents fired. A blue glow surrounded their guns, then engulfed them, instantly freezing them in place. The Patriot hurled his discs at the gloating Kaltherian, but they changed direction in mid air, exploding around his million-dollar computer system and smashing Keystone and Mass into a million frozen pieces.

"Did you really think we'd give you technology we couldn't control?!" laughed McLane/Urgo. "I hope you enjoy our little present. I know it would love to have *you* for dinner! Ah, ha, ha, ha, ha, ha!"

And with that, McLane/Urgo drew forth a gold and green disc and pressed the button. A white beam of light, which seemed to come straight through the ceiling, illuminated them. Then they were sucked up the length of the light, and they were gone as if they were never there.

"I had one of those," said Mark, recognizing the disc.

Scott got up to help the other Liberators.

"Scott! What'd they do with my stuff?!" Mark demanded, pulling him back with the cape.

"I don't know, sixth floor, evidence room probably," replied the Liberator. "Wait a minute, you got one of those?"

In the flagship, Dorothy pushed a hysterical half-woman, half-cheetah out of her way and aimed both her hands at the windshield of the spaceship.

"Buzz! Get down!"

Wafer thin laser beams shot through Dorothy's fingernails, heating the windshield from the inside and causing it to burst. She immediately climbed out with Buzz and organized the evacuation.

"Maser to all personnel, shoot through the windshield, it's your only chance!"

"No!" interrupted the Patriot. "If you destroy the ships, we'll never complete the mission!"

"The mission is aborted!" Dorothy overrode. "Do it, now!"

Inside ship two, Sven was fighting a losing battle against the goo.

"Sven!" squeaked Sea Hawk. "Blast the windshield!"

"The Son of Thor does not run from battle!" he insisted.

Just then, a wave of the goo grabbed the Liberator with the oversized head and stripped him to the bones before he could even scream. The Asgardian's eyes popped open to their fullest.

"Perhaps, just this once," said Sven, turning toward the windshield.

Sven blasted away the windshield, saving himself and four other Liberators. Scott opened up ship three, saving the pilot and co-pilot. Ship four was completely consumed and the goo from that ship, began to mingle with the other ships. Dorothy ordered the remains of the assault team to immediately retreat from the hangar.

The Patriot got to his feet and surveyed the situation. With goo already oozing out of the hangar, he rushed to a control panel, in the doorway of the adjoining room. He unlocked a secure switchbox and inserted a key.

From across the room, Maser and the remaining Liberators, were fighting against an increasingly stronger wave of goo. It sucked in the Liberator covered in purple flame, extinguishing him and his fire. Maser caught a glimpse of the Patriot.

"No! We're almost there!" she cried.

"Sorry, Dorothy, this thing has to be contained," he apologized flatly, hitting the switch.

All around the perimeter of the hangar and assembly room, the doors began to seal and lock. Upstairs, Mark and Scott had climbed out of the cell and were trying to find the way to a stairwell. At an emergency exit, they nearly ran into Smitty.

"I tried to find the door to the hangar," he said apologetically. "But I got stuck in the boiler room. I hit some switches so someone would come get me out, but I finally had to climb through a heating vent."

"Ya did good, Drunk Boy," smiled Mark, turning to Scott. "What's the fastest way to the sixth floor?"

"This stairwell only goes to four, we got to —"

Down the hall, Mark and Smitty noticed a large slab of concrete slowly lowering itself over the doorway. Even before he asked the question, Mark was moving forward.

"Is that good?" he asked Scott.

"No, that's the containment door," replied Scott, now worried for his own safety.

"Are we on the right side?" asked Smitty.

"Yeah—no! It's the other side," Scott said, diving for the door.

The threesome slid under, just as the door slammed.

"Aw, shit! I was right the first time," said Scott, upon seeing the inside of the sealed door.

"What are you, a fuckin' asshole?!" snapped Smitty.

Mark gestured for him not to prod the Liberator, but it was already too late.

"Hey, you want some of this?!" threatened Scott.

Scott and Smitty began to scuffle, with Mark in between, but just then, down the hall, the goo had bubbled up from an open hangar door and was heading their way.

"Hey! HEY!" objected Mark. "Oatmeal at ten o'clock!"

Mark ducked down a perpendicular hallway. Scott and Smitty, upon seeing the slithering mess approaching, followed.

Upstairs in the lobby, Mindy had finally poked her head out and found Goda, stirring on the floor nearby.

"Ee!" she squeaked in mild panic. "Mr. Goda? Can you hear me?"

"Yeah," he said reluctantly.

"Do you know if Mark is okay?"

Goda made a face, annoyed that she didn't even ask how he was. "Boy, you two are a freakin' match. As far as I know, he's fine."

"What happened?"

"One o' dese bags of shit got my boss. I forgot he played for Notre Dame in '78. Where are the officers that were waiting with you?"

At the same time, in an office not far from the hangar, Goda's fellow cybercop, Gene, was trying to get an official statement from Agent Garden. The Patriot's colonial was being less than cooperative. Darryl, Vincent and the three other officers, waited with bemused boredom at the red tape Garden kept throwing at them.

"All I need," said Gene for the fifth time. "Is *someone, anyone*, to sign a statement, so we can justify being out of the office for the last six hours!"

"And I keep telling you, this entire incident is classified and I'm not authorized to sign anything," stalled Garden. "Do you realize how secure this entire floor of offices is?"

Just then, Scott ran past the open doorway.

"No one even gets in here without direct authorization..."

Smitty followed, attracting Darryl's attention.

"...of the Patriot. You're only here because of this crisis and—-"

Out of breath, Mark slid to a halt in the doorway.

"We gotta get out of here," he panted and pointed back the way he came. "Big — *big* oatmeal."

"Get out of here!" snapped Garden.

"Wait up, we'll go with you," said Gene, gesturing to his men.

"You're not authorized to leave, yet," insisted Garden.

Just as the group got to the doorway, the goo came bubbling around the corner, this time it was picking up speed.

"Shit," said Gene in worried surprise. "Let's boogie."

Garden began walking deliberately toward the vile fluid.

"I wouldn't do that," warned Mark.

Garden removed his sunglasses, revealing his silvery pupils. His mass collapsed into the goo and disappeared into its mass.

"Unless, of course, you're one of them," finished Mark.

"I can't believe I just spent two hours talking to a bucket of pus," added Gene as they fled down the hall.

Meanwhile, the remaining Liberators had retreated to the furthest point away from the hangars. There were still three possible exits, but all were sealed by concrete containment doors. Dorothy pounded her access codes into one of the pads near a sealed door. Frustrated, she blew out the panel with a laser blast.

"That son of bitch already changed my codes! Sven! Can you bust down this thing?" she barked.

By this time, the pile of goo had expanded as far as the Patriot's computer system. It was eating through the console and monitors, sparking fires, which were immediately snuffed. Sven, Buzz, Seahawk and a handful of the other Liberators were blasting away at the tiny arms of the blob, but they were losing more ground than they gained. The woman with the tiny jet-pack, squealed in panic as her pack burst a seam and she plunged into the murky depths of death.

"Stand aside!" boomed Sven dramatically. "No mortal portal can hold back the Son of Thor!"

The mighty Asgardian's fingers plunged into the very stone foundation of the doorway. Lifting with thousands of tons of pressure, he strained as he pushed against the door's reinforced concrete and hydraulic steel deadbolts.

A few feet away, a door on the upper level flew open, as Mark and the others charged through and scrambled down a metal set of stairs. Almost immediately, a wave of goo came rushing out of the doorway after them, pushing office furniture and syrupy goo all over the catwalk and railings. Mark immediately walked over to Dorothy, who was over exerting herself trying to keep the wall of goo at bay.

"Usher, I can't find the exit in this theater," he quipped.

"Oh, great," she said unconvincingly. "*You're* still alive."

Darryl, Gene and the remaining cops fired into the growing pile of liquid in vain. A Liberator with bright yellow hair and orange skin ventured too close and was sucked into the mass. Mark knelt down next to Sven, who was still straining to lift the door.

"Sven?"

"Now is not the time!" he grunted.

"You're right, I didn't want to say anything," began Mark slyly. "But, uh, I heard frost giants can lift twice as much as Asgardians, is that true?"

The Liberators and the cops were now in a semi-circle around the door. The tiny island of goo-free space continued to shrink at an alarming rate.

"Your pathetic attempt at goading me, is not only insulting, but is distracting as well..."

As Sven continued to lift and talk, Mark was looking back and forth at an increasingly agitated pace. Overcome by sheer panic, he knelt next to Sven and bellowed directly into his ear, *"LIFT IIIIITTTTTT!!!!"*

Grimacing and eyes bulging wide, the world's mightiest hair stylist tore the containment door right off its hydraulic seals, nearly falling backwards as he did so.

"Go, go!" ordered Dorothy, not even waiting for him.

As the last free bit of the room shrank away to nothing and Liberator and policeman alike fled, Scott and Mark grabbed Sven by the shirt, keeping him from falling backward to certain death.

Upstairs, Patriot 13 grabbed the last of the classified documents he needed from the record's room on the fourth floor. Agent Rhodes was shredding documents as fast as the shredder could chew them.

"Good-bye, agent," said the Patriot flatly, heading for the door.

"Sir?" she began. "Has the situation in the basement been contained?"

"Of course, you're in no danger. Finish up here and we'll rendezvous at safe house 23," he assured.

"Yes, sir," she replied uneasily.

The Patriot got about ten steps from the elevator, when Goda and Mindy stepped off. Goda aimed his service revolver in his direction.

"Where do you think you're goin', you masked bag o' shit?"

"That's a classified matter, now I suggest you step aside."

"Where's Mark?!" demanded Mindy.

"And my men," added Goda.

"Dead, as will we be if we don't get out of here," insisted 13.

The Patriot took a few steps toward the elevators, but Goda gestured with his gun that that wouldn't be a good idea.

"I don't have time to explain it to you! This is a matter of national security! If you interfere, I'm authorized to throw you in jail for the rest of your miserable lives!"

"I don't think that's going to be much longer, thanks to you. Now start talkin'!" insisted Goda.

The Patriot relaxed. "I'm afraid you'll just have to shoot me."

"Don't tempt me!"

"I regret that I have but one life to give, for my country," he replied, condescendingly.

The Patriot waited patiently and after an awkward silence, Goda lowered the gun.

"You're not worth it," he hissed as he continued toward the elevator.

Smug in triumph, the Patriot walked past the elevators and toward the stairs.

"You're just letting him go?!" Mindy said indignantly.

"Keep out of this!" snapped Goda.

The stairwell door opened. Sven, Mark and the others walked through.

"You nearly deafened me!" complained Sven.

"It was a motivational speech," assured Mark. "You needed to be motivated."

The Patriot stopped in his tracks and met Dorothy's gaze. Scott, tried to push his way forward.

"Let me handle this," she insisted. "You're coming with me. And you're going to answer for every dead Liberator downstairs and your contacts in the State Department won't save you from it!"

"Dorothy," he replied, dripping with contempt. "Don't start a battle you can't finish. I've got a meeting with the president. Would any of you like to stop me?"

"Yeah, right," said Mark, amused.

"He won't tell us anything," added Goda reluctantly.

"You made the decision, Dorothy. You're the commander here, aren't you ultimately responsible, no matter how bad my intelligence was?" prodded the man behind the mask. "Now get out of the way."

The Liberators, terrified of the repercussions, looked away in fear. As the Patriot began to walk through the parting crowd, Mark snatched Darryl's pistol right out of its holster and jammed the barrel into the Patriot's mouth before anyone could stop him.

He roughly shoved the briefcase out of the Patriot's hand and forced him to the elevator doors.

"Hey-hey, Fix," Goda tried to soothe.

"Get off of me," growled Mark. "I'll do it, back off."

"You're a dead man, Fix," threatened the Patriot.

"Hey, that's right," agreed Mark, lifting up his other hand. "And I believe that's your fault, right? Would anyone miss this manipulative, backstabbing ass munch, if I blew his brains out right here?"

Mark paused for a reply, but was met by silence.

"I thought not. Open the doors, Sven."

Sven raised an eyebrow, not realizing Mark had it in him.

"Make it quick, lad," he added, forcing the doors open. "Not even he should suffer."

"Fix," warned Dorothy. "You don't know what you're doing..."

"Doesn't he?" countered Sven.

"Mark!" cried Mindy. "Stop!"

The detective forced the Patriot's head inside the elevator shaft. Several floors below, the semi-transparent goo was filling the space and slowly rising. The policemen and the Liberators stood motionless, suddenly no longer defined by their jobs. They were just people. People, who only moments ago, were sacrificed by an uncaring, faceless bureaucrat, who didn't even have the temerity to apologize for it.

"Oh, look," said Darryl, pretending to be distracted. "I think I'll look the other way. You see anything down this hall fellas?"

The other cops followed suit. Goda and the Liberators were uneasy, but did the same. This seemed only to encourage Mark to push the helpless Patriot further into the elevator shaft. Mark found him surprisingly frail for being so tall and thin, like an old man who was once an athlete.

The Patriot, however, said nothing. He knew it wouldn't help, he saw it in Mark's eyes. Struggling silently, he knew now death was inevitable. That it was just a matter of time before the detective decided to pull the trigger and shove his body down the shaft.

And for the first time, Mindy saw the death in Mark's eyes. She saw all the anger and hate for a hundred well up inside him like an overflowing black cauldron of rage. Now she knew, with all her heart, that Mark would kill for her and the thought would chill her to the bone for years to come. That look in his eyes. He'd kill the Patriot, and for her, he'd kill anyone that got in his way.

"Mark!" she squealed in terror. "Please! Don't do this! Please."

For a second, her words didn't seem to reach him.

"It's his fault, Min'. He didn't do it physically, but he set the wheels in motion that killed Viv and God knows how many others. And he doesn't even care. He's not even sorry! Why should somebody like that be allowed to live?"

"I don't know, but please, don't kill him," cried Mindy. "Just don't."

Mark gently set the hammer back and handed Darryl his gun back. The other Liberators pulled the Patriot away from the shaft. He was still quite shaken. Mark stared off into the distance, as if in a trance.

"I lied when I said I wouldn't kill for you, Min'," admitted Mark. "But mostly, I was afraid you'd see me like this."

"I'm sorry," Mindy wept. "It's my fault, I'm so sorry."

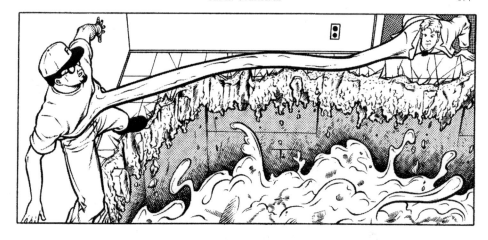

CHAPTER 36 (Narrator): Showdown City

Although the goo's progress had slowed down to less lethal levels, the Maine was quickly evacuated and its personnel sent home with little or no explanation. Dorothy regrouped the Liberators, along with Mark, Mindy, Smitty and Goda, at Sven's first salon two blocks away. Ironically, it was the previous site of the Liberators' HQ, before they went public. Sven had the top floors refurnished as his penthouse and the bottom two for his salon.

The salon itself was decorated with day glow barber chairs, several dozen large plants and an ornamental fountain dedicated to the goddess Sif. Buzz and Scott were using the salon phones to contact whatever Liberators were left in Philadelphia, while Bryan, one of Sven's stylists, attempted to help in his own way.

"Thighs of Thor, Bryan!" he bellowed. "The fate of the world is at stake! I need you to call any available Liberator in my rolodex! Now, get to work and stop making tea!"

"Well, I just thought it would help you relax!" cried Bryan, stamping his foot, setting down his tray of tea and scones, then marching away.

Sven frowned in frustration at his overly sensitive employee. The Patriot, tied to one of the barber chairs, smirked in contempt.

"Interesting that you turned the old Liberator headquarters into a tacky shrine dedicated to conceit and vanity. Poetic justice, I suppose."

"You will hold your tongue or I will cut it out and nail it to the archway for all to see!" threatened Sven.

Across the room, SeaHawk knocked over a display of bottles.

"Oh, blast," muttered Sven, distracted, moving away. "The mousse."

Dorothy spun the Patriot around to face her and Goda. From across the room, Mark, Mindy and Smitty watched. Mark's hand was wrapped in a makeshift bandage, which now constantly dripped into a bucket than Sven provided. He looked pale and his eyes were sunken in.

"This ship you gave the Kaltherians," said Dorothy, interrogating the Patriot. "Where is it?"

The Patriot was still not forthcoming, but Dorothy squeezed his arm and looked at him threateningly.

"If I knew, I would tell you. It doesn't matter now, it's already been launched," he explained. "Its payload is enormous, but it's mostly fuel for the trip home."

"Unless they don't go anywhere," added Dorothy. "In which case, how long before they run out of fuel?"

"If the rate of consumption in the ships they helped us build was any indication," he said grimly. "Three, maybe four weeks."

A wave of despair rippled through the group.

"Weeks?!"

"That's why I have to leave now," insisted the Patriot. "The president has to act, before it's too late."

"Nuke Philadelphia?"

"It's the only way to save the rest of the country," said the Patriot, with every ounce of regret he could muster. "It could already be too late."

"Hold it, what about the stadium?" interrupted Mark. "Gornon said they were planning to do something to the stadium. There's a game at the Vet tonight, right?"

"Yeah and if he got a few fat guys in, like the ones on the ship," continued Goda.

"I know what he's doing," said Smitty, suddenly lucid again. "He's trying to grow a Kalther."

"No," gasped the Patriot in realization.

"He doesn't need the stadium, he needs the people in it," explained Smitty.

"That's essentially one of you guys, only bigger?" asked Mindy, trying to understand.

"Kinda, Kalthers can grow to be the size of continents, but they need a lot of protein. The second they stop eating, they begin to die, like the one in the Maine building."

"Dorothy," added Mark, increasingly worried. "If even one of those fat men get through the gate..."

"There'd be no stopping it," finished Smitty. "A Kalther that size could spread over the whole city."

"Min'," Mark said in discomfort. "I'm really feeling awful, could you run up to Sven's bathroom and find me some aspirin?"

"Yeah, sure," she complied, eager to make up for earlier.

"Dorothy," insisted Mark. "You got to get what's left of the team to Vet stadium, right now."

"If you're wrong about this —"

"There's no time left anyway," interrupted Mark.

"He's right," added Goda. "We can't nuke Philly anyways, my property tax is already too high."

"Good one," smiled Mark.

"All right," Dorothy exhaled. "Liberators! Let's move!"

As the last remnants of Goda's precinct and the Liberators prepared to move out, Mark pulled Goda to the side.

"Goda, you gotta make sure Mindy gets home okay," Mark said in a half daze, trying to stay awake. "I got one final play to make and I don't want her to see me like this, 'kay?"

"Yeah, sure," Goda said somberly.

"C'mon Drunk Boy," Mark gestured to Smitty.

Mark got off his chair and nearly tumbled over. Smitty steadied him as he walked out.

"Hey, Fix, uh," Goda called after him. "Nice workin' with ya."

"Yeah, well, umm," stammered Mark, unused to compliments on his detective work. "Better get hoppin'. Get it? One leg—Hoppin'..."

Goda made a sour face. Darryl followed him outside and stifled a giggle.

"You know," he said to Darryl thoughtfully. "I was almost gonna miss him."

Upstairs, Mindy was going through Sven's medicine cabinet, but all she could find were dried jars of roots and leaves.

"Where does a Viking keep his aspirin?!" she said in frustration.

Giving up, she closed the mirror cabinet and was surprised by Smitty, who was standing right behind her with a grim expression on his face.

"Jesus!" she said with a start. "Don't do that."

"Forget the aspirin," he said flatly. "I want to show you something."

At the same time, just outside, Goda was about to step into a police car, when he spotted a man watching the cars in front of the salon. He was carrying a long, black duffel bag and was fumbling to get something out of it. A homeless man sleeping on the sidewalk nearby, scrambled to get away from him.

"Lieutenant, c'mon," said Darryl.

"Take off," ordered Goda. "Now!"

When the man completely turned around, he looked amazingly like a nineteen-year-old Unger Jenkinson, trying to pull a missile launcher out of his Baltimore Mustangs duffle bag. Goda whipped out his pistol and began firing. The bullets passed harmlessly through the quarterback.

"Your bullets cannot harm me, human!" he taunted, preparing to aim for the Liberator van down the street.

"I'm not aimin' at you," growled Goda.

His third shot went down the barrel of the missile launcher and ignited the explosive. The explosion knocked Goda off his feet and broke windows in a two-block radius. The Patriot, helpless in the chair, caught some of the flying glass in his face, but the explosion shook his chair loose. He quickly recovered and freed himself. In front of the Maine, Smitty caught up to Mark, then turned at the noise.

"Did you bring your gun?" asked Smitty.

"I lost it," explained Mark, putting his one arm over Smitty's shoulder to steady himself.

"You *lost* it?!"

"It'll turn up eventually. Where did you go?"

Somewhere on Broad Street, the remaining Liberators and policemen, sped toward Veterans Stadium. Philadelphia was playing Austin, their arch rivals since the early Eighties'. Thousands of fans packed the Vet to cheer on the home team, but if Gornon's plan was set in motion, it wouldn't be the only massacre they saw that day.

"Sven," asked Dorothy, hanging on for dear life. "Maybe you should let me drive."

"Fear not!" he assured. "A true warrior is at the wheel!"

Bottoming out at the next intersection, the Liberator's van nearly went airborne. Dorothy steadied herself against the back of Sven's seat while taking stock of her remaining forces. Buzz, Seahawk, Scott, Sven, herself and six other Liberators, all with moderate to low powers, plus ten police officers whom she considered nothing but cannon fodder for the battle ahead. They were about five blocks from the Vet when they saw them.

"By the gods..." gasped Sven.

Larry Hern (from his '75 champion days), Guy Frenzo (who looked sixteen years younger), Trent Jordan ("Lucky Seven"), Jack Robertson ("the Polish Rifle"), Donnie Thompson (thirty-three years young again), Dan Thorbird (without the career-ending leg injury he got in Super Bowl XVII), Willy Rapp (minus the ninety-two pounds he'd gained since retiring), Reed Johnson (the Eighties' star running back), Sam Gander ("40oz Sam"), Bill Glickman (whose sixteen kicks won the Super Bowl), the cheerleaders from Dallas, the entire defensive line for Oakland and dozens of football's finest had surrounded the Vet. Each one had a mercury gaze that cut right past the wary pedestrians, who were beginning to notice the heavily armed football players. Actually, they were all armed except ex-Philadelphia quarterback, Robertson, who was the real thing and had come to see the game.

"I thought today was a regular game," he said to his wife curiously.

"It's like a walkin' Hall of Fame out there!" exclaimed Scott.

Dorothy's telescopic vision zeroed in on what looked like Martin Wink. Washington's number one quarterback had just pulled a pin on a hand grenade.

"Sven, look out!"

Dorothy grabbed the wheel of the van, veering it into a parked pick up. Behind them, Darryl skidded to a halt and the grenade rolled under a parked Hunsai.

"Out of the van!"

KA-BOOM!

As the Polish Rifle and his wife fled the hail of bullets, the Kaltherian football players quickly surrounded the last hope for humanity.

Inside the Maine, Mark and Smitty searched the empty offices for the evidence room and Mark's trenchcoat.

"That's the last room, do you think they hid it?" asked the alien.

"I don't know," Mark exhaled, trying to stay focused. "Maybe he said the seventh floor..."

"Didn't you listen to what he said? Duh! You're supposed to remember these things, what kind of detective are you?"

"I remember, I remember," insisted Mark. "It was a floor with an F in it. Fourth, fifth... Wait a minute, floor has an F in it. Maybe it was six. Six rhymes with Fix."

There was a low rumble and suddenly, the doors at the end of the hallway burst open. A wave of goo surged towards them.

"Ah! You said it was dead!" objected Mark.

"Well, it's *almost* dead."

Smitty was practically dragging Mark now. He pulled him into a stairwell and up to the sixth floor. Agent Rhodes, finally finished with her shredding, was already standing in the hallway.

"You!" she said reaching for her gun.

They ducked into a side office and a bullet smacked the doorjamb just after they entered. Inside was row after row of nameless cubicles used for the drones that handled the Liberators payroll and finances.

"People are always shooting at you," said Smitty, annoyed.

"Me?" corrected Mark. "She was aiming for you. *I'd* aim for you."

Somewhere near the room that housed the Liberator's computer network, Rhodes ran past an unassuming filing cabinet. After she had rounded a corner, it morphed off of

Mark and reformed into Smitty. Mark was completely weirded out by the experience.

"That was creepy, man," he whispered in disgust. "Next time, just let me hide in the closet."

"Aw, c'mon," said Smitty, a little hurt. "I do a really cool credenza."

Just then the whole room shifted. Mark lost his footing and slid out of the doorway and into a vending machine in the hall. The building settled and Smitty ran after him.

"Are you okay?" asked the alien.

"Oh, my God!" said Mark, in disbelief. "Half this vending machine is full of toffee bars! Do people actually *eat* those?"

"I guess."

"Smitty," said Mark, regaining his composure. "Could that big blob thing downstairs eat through the foundation of the building?"

Smitty thought about it for a second, realized he forgot something terribly important, looked down at his shoes and then back at Mark.

"Did I forget to tell you that?" said the alien meekly. "Cause I thought I did."

"Yes! Yes!" said the detective sarcastically. "That was just a *tiny* tidbit of information *you might've passed on to us!*"

"C'mon," said Smitty. "Fuck this saving the world. Let's just go find some beer and strippers before we die."

"No, no, you save the world first, then the beer and strippers."

In another part of the building, Agent Rhodes let her eyes turn silver, than began to morph into another person.

Mark and Smitty stumbled down another hall, turned away from the hall that Agent Rhodes was standing in, then circled back and stumbled upon a door marked "Evidence Room".

"Finally," said Mark impatiently, barreling through the door.

Inside, the evidence room had collapsed into the floors below. Smitty caught Mark and pulled him back into the hallway. Below, the dying Kalther continued to ooze and seep, waiting for another morsel of food to blunder into its path. Office furniture, debris and bodies littered its interior like some kind of weird, giant head cheese. Across the thirty-foot expanse, Mark's trenchcoat, holster and gun were on a table in preparation to be tagged for his future incarceration.

"Quick-quick-quick, reach over and get it," insisted Mark.

Smitty's arm elongated across the expanse, but he was rapidly depleting his own mass to reach it. Below, the Kalther suddenly became agitated and began to bubble. Tiny psuedo pods rose up out of its mass, sensing the presence of one of its own. A mere four feet away, Smitty suddenly retracted his arm.

"C'mon!" squealed Mark. "You almost had it! I got confidence in you, man! C'mon!"

"It's not that," explained Smitty, his inner demons already quieted. "I can't reach it and the Kalther knows I'm here. If I go into the room, it could rise up and swallow the whole room."

Mark knew what was coming next and muttered to himself in objection.

"Just walk around the edges, I'll try and hold you up. All you have to do is get halfway across and I think the floor will hold."

"Maaaaaan," said Mark, not wanting to go.

Cautiously, Mark's sneakers slid against what was left of the buckled concrete of the evidence room. Every so often, crumbling pieces of steel and cement fell into the monster below causing tiny ripples in its surface. Smitty's extended arm helped hold Mark up, but he was clearly drained and was now struggling just to stay conscious.

"I can't do this," he panted. "I gotta rest."

"C'mon, Fat boy," urged Smitty. "Do it for the Second Floor. Do it for America. For ma, pa and apple pie."

"Hate apple pie," slurred Mark.

One of Mark's foot slipped and Smitty pushed him back up with both hands.

"Okay, okay, do it for *Mindy*," mocked the alien. "Mindy, I'm coming. Mindy, I'll drop whatever I'm doing to see you. Mindy, I'm so whipped I'll wipe your butt."

"Shut up," Mark said more determined.

"I can't go out tonight, fellas," mocked Smitty. "Mindy wants me to stay home and help her douche. By the way, she keeps my penis under lock and key."

With what little strength he had left in his legs and arms, Mark stumbled to the other side of the room. Slightly energized, he put back on his trenchcoat, holster and gun. He reached into the pocket, pulled out a plastic fork and tossed it away. In his other pocket was the gold and green disc.

"All right!" said Smitty. "I didn't think that would work, cause you just did the same thing to Sven and——"

"When I get back over there," said Mark still angry. "I'm gonna shoot you. I told you not to talk that way about Mindy!"

"No, Mark it was just to get you to——"

As if on cue, Mindy stepped into the hallway.

"Oh, great!" Mark said exasperated, throwing his hands into the air. "Speak of the Devil and she appears. What are you doing here, Min'?"

"I *insisted* she come," said the Patriot, stepping into view. "You've interfered with my plans for the last time, Fix!"

The Patriot kept his gun pointed at Mindy's head.

"Wait, wait!" pleaded Mark. "You don't have to do this. I have something, we can beat the Kaltherians."

Mark showed him the green and gold disc.

"I got this off of one of them," he explained. "You push it and you go right to their ship. If you tied a nuke to it, ka-boom, capiche? Here, you can have it, be the big hero, I don't care, just let us go."

"Fine," said the Patriot, irritated. "Throw it here."

Mark looked down at the Kalther and then around the room.

"Maybe I should bring it over," he suggested.

"You're only thirty feet away, son," the irritated Patriot acknowledged. "There's nothing in your way, how can you miss?!"

"Oh! I hate when people say that," added Mark. "Because then you know I'm gonna miss and——"

The Patriot jammed the gun back in Mindy's ear.

"Just throw it!"

Mark tossed the disc. It klinked against the edge of the floor near the doorway, then bounced and landed on a ledge on the floor below.

"See? See?!" said Mark, trying to justify it.

"Idiot," snapped the Patriot, letting Mindy go. "It almost went in."

As the Patriot reached over, Smitty gestured to Mark as if to say, "Should I push him in?". Mark weighed the option, then shook his head "no".

"Step away from them," ordered Goda.

Goda, bruised and banged after the explosion, limped his way up the corridor. His cybernetic leg had been damaged in the blast and metals and wires were exposed where his pants were torn.

"Goda?" shouted Mark, trying to see him. "Who do you mean?"

"I'm talkin' about the Patriot," he shouted back. "The real one had a change of heart and called in the cavalry."

At that moment, the Liberators and the cops were fending off the Kaltherian/PFL attack. They were pinned near the burning wreck of the Liberator van. Scott and two of the officers had been shot. Buzz lay unconscious from another explosion and both Dorothy and Sven were just about out of fight.

When it seemed the Kaltherians would close in for the kill, the 38th Armored Division, on maneuvers on a base just outside the city, roared into the Vet's parking lot with the Patriot in the lead car. By this time, the Kaltherians had used up most of their ammo, and the rapid fire machine guns from the jeeps and armored vehicles made short work of the aliens, striking them in so many places at once, they couldn't move their vital organs away from harm. A cheer went up from the beleaguered warriors and Sven led the charge from their hiding spot.

"The tide of battle turns swiftly our way!"

"Yeah!" agreed Scott. "Let's toast 'em! I think I see Robertson!"

Inside Vet stadium, Don and Russ, two diehard Philadelphia fans, prepared to drink beer and eat their hotdogs, while enjoying the opening kick off from the worst seats in history.

"I think my nose is bleeding," said Don with a mouthful of dog.

"I know," agreed Russ. "Did you hear an explosion?"

"Yeah," said Don. "We'll have to check it out after the game."

As the opening kick commenced, an enormously fat fan took his seat behind them.

Back in the Maine, Gornon/Patriot dropped his disguise, letting his eyes turn the color of Mercury. He grabbed Mindy again.

"Shoot all you like," he smiled. "I have such a pretty shield. I think I'll show her the ship, wouldn't want to get nuked while I was destroying your world."

"Smitty, get 'em!" insisted Mark.

Gornon/Patriot laughed, "Come now, Rojbor, don't make a fuss. The rest of the crew misses you. You don't belong here anyway."

"There's no other fleet it's been all you from the beginning," deduced Goda.

"Well, at least one of you is a detective," laughed Gornon/Patriot.

Smitty grabbed Gornon's gun. He fired, narrowly missing Goda. Mark took cover behind a bookshelf, which suddenly shifted and then fell into the Kalther below.

"Don't make a fuss, Rojbor," Gornon/Patriot said annoyed. "You belong with your own kind."

Gornon/Patriot pulled forth his own gold and green disc and pushed the button.

"Mindy, jump!"

"What do you think I've been trying to do?!" she snapped, suddenly encased in a beam of white light.

Goda dived for the threesome, but they disappeared. Mark was trying to make his way back, but the building shifted again. The whole evidence room and the rooms above were collapsing in on themselves toward the Kalther. The more debris that fell into it, the more it seemed to weaken the building. Goda made a reach for the green and gold disc, but it seemed just out of his reach.

"Do you got it? Do you got it?!" asked Mark impatiently.

"Shut up," growled Goda.

"C'mon, Long John Sipowitz, grab the disc!"

A section of building suddenly folded under Goda. He slid into the room, but caught himself on a length of steel support. Now he was even closer to the disc.

"Hang on, man, hang on!" said Mark.

"Can't...get a grip," panted Goda, sliding down the piece of steel.

"Get ready," said Mark, preparing to leap.

"No! Don't!"

Mark jumped and extended just enough to grab Goda. He fell off the support and was hanging by his fingertips. The Kalther below was bubbling upwards, sensing Mark's presence. Just as Goda lost his grip, Mark reached for the disc and pushed the button as they fell. Mere inches from the man-eating menace, a beam of white light sucked them into oblivion.

Almost instantly, they were standing inside the Kaltherian ship, but neither Mark or Goda had time to access the situation. The twosome were too busy gasping for air, like beached fish. Mindy and Smitty lay unconscious against the wall near the doorway, while Gornon/Victor and six guys who looked exactly like the New York's defensive line, stood with knowing expressions on their faces.

"Did I forget to tell you?" said Gornon in mock concern. "We lowered air pressure so it would be like a Kaltherian vessel. It's *much* higher than Earth, even Rojbor wasn't used to it."

Goda wheezed, dropped his gun and passed out. Mark thought he had a heart attack, but couldn't do anything, except swoon and fall face first to the floor.

"Welcome aboard!" beamed Gornon sinisterly.

<u>CHAPTER 37</u> (Narrator): Ship of Pools

When Mark came to, he didn't know how long he'd been out, but was surprised to be awakened by a stiff breeze. He was strapped to the side of, for all intents and purposes, a flying saucer built from army surplus parts. The entire ship resembled a camouflaged football, dotted here and there with the words "U.S. Army" stenciled in white letters. Mark was pinned at both wrists with what looked like metal cuffs, which had been specially placed there just for him. A man who looked exactly like a linebacker from Atlanta, was finishing affixing the left cuff.

The ship was hovering a thousand feet above an expanse of trees unfamiliar to Mark. Gornon/Victor and a man who looked exactly like Denver's quarterback, Ed Jewett, stood at the rim of the ship seven yards away, admiring the view.

"Commander," said Jewett, gesturing to Mark.

"Oh, good," said Gornon/Victor smugly. "I'm glad you're awake. I wanted to make this personal."

Mark coughed up a huge chunk of phlegm, which ran down his cheek at a speed all its own. Squinting at Gornon/Victor, he noticed he was sweating the same kind of phlegm.

"Look at him Urgo," Gornon/Victor gesture to Jewett. "The last hope for the human race. Pathetic, isn't it?"

"Sir, do we really have to have it on the ship?" Urgo/Jewett said uncomfortably.

"Where's Mindy?" Mark managed to say.

"With your one-legged friend. Fascinating device, his leg. I think we'll keep him to study and the female—-" he said, thinking. "I think she'd make a nice pet or snack. Or I might just toss her out of the airlock for a laugh, I haven't decided."

"Airlock, airlock," urged Urgo/Jewett.

Gornon/Victor and Mark both simultaneously got nauseous. Urgo/Jewett, steadied his commander, and helped him to his feet.

"I'm fine, I'm fine!" he insisted.

"He's not fine," Mark wheezed. "He's dying just like me. You're all dying."

Urgo/Jewett looked toward Gornon/Victor, the alien commander's eyes shifted with worry.

"Is that true?" asked Urgo/Jewett, with urgency.

"Of course, not, if one of us lives, we *all* live," countered Gornon.

"Yeah, but for how long?" asked Mark. "How long had you been at it, Gornon? Splitting off from Smitty and then dying before you had a chance to save yourself, much less recreate your crew. You've been trying since the crash forty years ago."

"Forty years!" said Urgo in astonishment. "We've been here that long? You never said —"

"It didn't matter!" insisted Gornon. "I don't know how you know that, but its true. Every few years Rojbor would accumulate enough mass to split and recreate me, but he was always too drunk to notice. Mere hours after I was recreated, my cell structure would break down."

"You set up the medical experiments and hunted for the right human DNA. The same that allowed Smitty's cell structure to stay stable," continued Mark. "Then the killings started —"

"We couldn't screen them fast enough! Examining the livers was the fastest way!" insisted Gornon. "We had no choice!"

"Yeah, but you did all that and it still didn't work, until you came up with the microbe. You stuck it in the heroin. The junkies just got eaten up or dropped dead."

"Yes, I could create dozens of copies of me simultaneously, each one lasting longer and longer until finally..."

"Victor," continued Mark. "But even he screwed it up for you, when he injected me with part of the microbe."

"No!"

"Oh, yeah. You're only half the man you used to be and since all your boys were split from you, it's just a matter of time before you all fall to pieces," smiled Mark.

Of course, Mark hadn't put it together himself, the Stuff had told him everything.

"How could you know all that?" said Urgo, astonished at Mark's knowledge. "Not even I —"

"He's just taunting us, Urgo," Gornon explained. "Yes, human, we are dying, but I've had enough time to recreate the microbes for an elder Kalther. All it needs is the right amount of protein. When the Kalther consumes the city below, it will be large enough to contain its own ecosystem and we will tend to it. It will restore our bodies and we'll no longer need Rojbor's DNA."

"Think so, huh?" smiled Mark knowingly. "I believe your fat boys are in for a big surprise."

"Oh, really?" smiled Gornon.

Back at Veterans stadium, Dorothy and the Patriot led the 38th Armored Division in sweeping the stands for anyone over three-hundred pounds. The Patriot reached the seats where Don and Russ sat.

"You!" ordered the Patriot, his two marine sidekicks pointing their guns. "Don't move!"

Russ and Don turned back to get a glimpse at who they were capturing. An enormously overweight man with a mustache shrugged and took a sip of his beer.

"Moving's not exactly on the top of my list, pal," said the fat man snidely.

Back on the ship, Gornon gestured for Mark to look over the side. Below was not the Vet, but Meadowlands stadium. Mark could see the letters G-I-A and N, just past the edge of the ship and clearly visible behind the goal line. Thousands of NY fans and several weird looking fat men had crowded the stands.

"Do you know what that means?" the alien asked in triumph.

"Uh, Philadelphia is playing New York?" Mark asked, not realizing the situation.

"No, you idiot! That's the Meadowlands down there!"

"Oh, my God..."

"Yes! You were right, Philadelphia was just an experiment. And with the Liberators miles away, they haven't a chance of stopping this."

"Victor," Mark called to him desperately. "You've got to still be in there. Fight him! He's weakening!"

"You're a little late for that, human!" said the alien amused.

The former coach for Philadelphia stuck his head out a hatch and looked in Gornon's direction.

"Commander, we're almost in position," he informed him.

Jewett/Urgo, Gornon and the others headed back inside the ship.

"By the way that's a maneuvering thruster we've strapped you to," explained Gornon. "In about ten seconds you're going to be vaporized!"

"Big whoop, I'm dead anyway."

"Well, if that doesn't impress you. Maybe I'll just bomb your house before we start," he threatened.

"Hey, leave my folks out of this!" objected Mark.

"Folks? You still live with your *parents*?" Gornon said incredulously. "Ah, ha, ha, ha, ha, ha, ha!"

Mark grimaced angrily, as the alien's sinister laugh faded into the ship. The detective began squirming frantically, rubbing against the inside of his trenchcoat.

"The jokes on him," thought Mark. "The heat won't touch me, the force of the thruster is what will kill me. His boys will be cleaning me off the ship for *weeks*."

Inside the ship, Goda and Mindy sat strapped to army surplus jeep seats and forced to watch the destruction of their planet through a window behind Gornon's bridge. Smitty stood grimly nearby, a small one-celled organism sat on his chest, completely paralyzing him. If he could cry, he would've been tearing buckets. On the monitors in front of him, Gornon directed the action and Urgo stood nearby.

"Prepare maneuvering thrusters," ordered Gornon.

"Smitty!" screamed Mindy. "Do something."

"Please, Commander," begged Smitty. "Gornon. The invasion's over..."

"This isn't about the invasion," Gornon admitted. "It's about survival."

"We don't have to do this! Let's just go home! I'll go with you, leave the humans—_"

"We have no home! Our planet is dead!" he snapped.

Outside the ship, Mark could see the engines ignite in the bowels of the ship. He continued to squirm more frantically.

"We didn't join the invasion to Earth for profit," continued Gornon. "We did it for survival. The Elder Kalthers were out of food. It's part of our natural cycle, we need to be recreated on another planet."

"B-but, that can't be true," stammered Smitty.

"How could we build a ship big enough to move a continent? This is the only way Rojbor. Relax. We won't have to do it again for at least a thousand years. Excuse me.

Urgo, fire the thrusters."

Just as the engines began to roar with life and a ball of white of flame shot down the length of the maneuvering thruster, Mark managed to trigger his sleeve holster. Instantly, the package of salad dressing shot into his hand. He squeezed it until it burst, letting the oily mess cover right hand. A little splashed on his face and he tasted it with his tongue.

"Mmm, Catalina," he noted.

The blast roared past him, just as he pulled his arm free. The column of heat caused his trenchcoat to burst into flame. Mark quickly reached into his hat and swallowed the vial of green Stuff he had hidden inside during his stop at home. As his eyes glowed green, he was engulfed in flame and, as an afterthought, shoved his hat into his mouth.

Inside the ship, Gornon seemed to breath a sigh of relief. The pains and episodes he was experiencing earlier had suddenly stopped.

"Ah," he said, pleased with himself. "He's dead, I can feel it."

Below, in the Meadowlands stadium, an enormously fat man began drooling disgusting goo all over himself. Two NY fans sitting near him, who looked very similar to Don and Russ, gave him an odd look.

"Musta hadda hotdog," the first concluded to the second.

"All right," said Gornon, comfortably sliding into his position as Commander.

"Shall we re-pressurize the ship, Commander?" asked a Los Angeles cheerleader.

"Later," replied Gornon, waving her off. "How many units do we have down there?"

"Fifty-one," responded Chicago's Buck Daniels, routinely. "But only half are inside."

"Is that enough?" Gornon turned to Jewett/Urgo.

"Stop it! Stop it!" screamed Mindy in hysterics.

Urgo was about to respond, but made an annoyed face as Mindy interrupted him. Gornon pressed a button and Mindy's screams faded.

"Definitely, airlock," added Gornon. "Move the ship into position."

Somewhere on the other side of the ship, Mark, completely naked, climbed back into the ship. He closed the hatch behind him, ducked into a side room and made sure none of the busy Kaltherian/football players noticed him. Sure that he was safe, he dry heaved a few times and hacked up his baseball hat. His eyes continued to glow a bright green.

"Blaugh," he whispered in disgust.

He looked at his hand, it was now completely free of goo. Only the Kaltherian microbe had been vaporized, while unbelievably he was completely unscathed. As he examined his hand, he noticed his fingernails growing at an alarming rate.

"Oh, great," he said aloud forgetting where he was for the moment. "Like *this* is gonna help me."

Hearing his last statement, Pete Jansen stopped in the hallway, and walked toward the noise sixteen feet away. The Oakland quarterback surprised Mark and caused a tiny Kaltherian pistol to shoot out of his arm and into his hand. Helpless, Mark put his hands up to shield himself.

"No, don't!" he objected.

Before Jansen could pull the trigger, Mark's fingernails ejected themselves right off his fingertips with lethal velocity. Caught unawares, one of the fingernails hit Jansen's vital organ and he expired into a pile of mush. Mark put his arms over his head, shielding himself from the ricocheting fingernails.

"Hey," said Mark, reexamining his hands with interest.

His fingernails sprouted up to their previous lengths and continued to grow. Mark pointed them away from himself.

Urgo checked Gornon's calculations on a modified PC. He opened a window on his screen labeled "Earth Destroyer!" and double clicked an icon of a little exploding globe. Urgo inserted a CD into the CD-Rom drive. A graphic of a red button appeared and was labeled "Send signal".

"We're in position," informed the most recent number one PFL draft pick.

"Good," noted Gornon, turning to Urgo. "Are we ready yet?"

"All I have to do is click the mouse, sir."

"Do it."

Just as Urgo clicked the mouse, there was a drop in power, the computer shut down for a second and began to reboot.

"What was that?!" bellowed Gornon.

"We had a drop in power, I have to reboot," explained Urgo.

Furious, Gornon tore himself out of his chair and stomped to a monitoring station operated by the coach of Miami.

"I don't understand, commander," he said, flustered. "Everything was working perfectly."

Somewhere in the ship, Mark had found some important looking power cables.

"I'm, ooooh, I'm still alive," he sung quietly in his bad imitation of the PJ song.

Mark zapped them with the gun he got off of Jansen and the cable exploded. At the same time, his fingernails reached maximum length and fired in the direction his fingers were pointing. Mark grimaced as he was covered with tiny little scratches from his own fingernails.

At the same time, behind Gornon, the power surge had loosened the automatic restraints that kept Mindy in place. She cautiously pulled her arms out. Goda's restraints were also loose, but not enough so he could get free immediately.

"I think I can get out," she whispered to Goda.

"Don't worry about me, get in there, crash the ship, do what you can," said Goda quickly.

"Count on it," she said determined.

"Commander, we've scanned an intruder in the lower level it's — It's Fix," said the mascot for St. Louis in disbelief.

"What?!" screamed Gornon. "That's impossible!"

"It's him, I confirm the reading," added Urgo calmly.

"Turn the pressure back up! Suffocate all of them!"

"It'll take twenty minutes. We lost pressure when you opened the —"

"Forget it! Will somebody just go down there and *kill* that idiot?!" screamed Gornon.

"You said he was just a human," Urgo pointed out. "That thruster was over three thousand degrees—-"

"I don't know how he did it, just run the program!"

Just as Urgo slid in the CD-Rom and prepared to click the mouse, Mindy barged into the room. Before any of the Kaltherians could react, she dove, slid across the floor and reached for the plug.

"No!" said Urgo, seeing her out of the corner of his eye.

He let loose a flurry of tentacles, which pinned Mindy against the wall, but not before she pulled the plug. She held onto the cord and began pulling the computer off its console.

"Stop!"

Urgo stopped pushing her, but kept his slimy arms around her.

"Let go of me!" insisted Mindy. "Let go or it hits the floor."

Urgo let her go and the Kaltherians back away, keeping their pistols trained on her. Distracted, Mark charged in and aimed his pistol at Gornon. He was wearing his baseball cap over his penis.

"Well, well, well, well," smiled Mark, as the guns turned in his direction. "Mexican stand off, anyone?"

Gornon, livid that his plan was unraveling, looked around the room for someone to vent on.

"Forty years of planning and no one bothered to lock the door?!" he lamented.

Gornon turned and looked at Mark with growing interest.

"You survived the microbe," he said in astonishment. "It consumed better than one quarter of your mass and yet, you're completely cured. HOW?!"

"Just drop your weapons!"

"Shoot him!"

"Shoot him and I drop the computer!"

"In that case," explained Gornon, cautiously moving toward Smitty. "I will shoot him."

"You're not gonna shoot him," scoffed Mark.

"Won't I? If I shoot Rojbor, we'll all die and you'll be responsible not just for our deaths, but that of an entire planet. Are you prepared to make that sacrifice?"

Mark swallowed nervously, he wasn't even sure he could make the shot and his fingernails were getting uncomfortably long again.

"Don't worry about me, Mark," Smitty said sadly. "Maybe its better this way."

There was an awkward silence, broken only by Mindy's squeal of frustration. Mark looked Gornon in the eye and made his decision.

"Actually," he smiled. "I don't think anyone has to die."

Mark's fingernails shot out of his fingers in various directions, causing everyone in the room to duck and cover. Using the distraction, the PI fired his gun into what looked like the helm console for the ship. The ship lurched and than began its descent.

"There," he said triumphantly, noting the parking lot stadium just outside the window. "It's all over. We'll crash-land in the parking lot and you can't activate the Kalther because you'll be too close."

"You *IDIOT!*" spat Gornon, his eyes blazing. "You're looking at the wrong monitor. That's a remote video camera we left at the stadium. *That's* outside the ship!"

Mark turned his gaze to the screen just to the left of where he was looking. He could see the East Coast, the various states and the cloud formations above them.

"We're *TEN MILES UP!*" screamed Gornon. "You've killed us all!"

Mark's internal soundtrack needle skittered across the surface of his imaginary piece of vinyl, leaving him momentarily stymied.

"Oh," he mumbled in surprise. "My bad."

Urgo yanked the power chord from Mindy's grasp, picked her up and tossed her into the room. Buck Daniels, the Los Angeles cheerleader and the St. Louis mascot began firing at Mark, who ducked behind Gornon's command chair.

"Start the program!" snapped Gornon, unconcerned with anything else.

Buck Daniels had morphed across the floor of the room and reformed behind Mark, but Goda charged into the room, belted him, took his gun and turned it on him, before he could react.

"Mindy!" screamed Mark. "Get behind me!"

"Die human!" bellowed Gornon.

Gornon shot forth an arm, which ended in a point, plunging through Mindy's back and out her chest. She collapsed next to Mark with a surprised squeak.

"MINDY!" cried Mark, aiming his gun at Gornon. "YOU ASSHOLE!"

He fired, hitting the window to the outside. It immediately was covered by a thin layer of ice and cracked under the pressure. Several of Oakland's offensive line were sucked out of the crack before they could get a grip on something heavy. The two doors that led to the bridge automatically began to slide closed when the air pressure dropped. Goda jammed his cybernetic leg between them open. Mark wanted to charge over and kill Gornon with his bare hands, but Goda still managed to pull him back under cover.

"Stay down!"

Goda provided cover for the moment, Mark was consumed by grief.

"Mindy, oh-God-oh-God," he cried cradling her head and kissing her. "You can't die..."

"It's okay, Mark," she assured.

"I love you, Min', I love you, don't go..."

"Mark —"

"I can't live without you," he sobbed.

The hole in Mindy's chest closed by itself and Mark was suddenly cradling Smitty.

"I wuv you, Mindy," mocked the alien.

Mark's eyes were full of fire.

"Yooooouuuu, asshole!"

As Mark began choking Smitty, Goda looked back to the other Smitty standing in the center of the room, paralyzed.

"Wait a minute," he said suspiciously.

Straining, the other Smitty ripped off the paralyzing mite, drew forth two Kaltherian pistols out of his body and took his true form. Goda immediately recognized him.

"Coach!"

Urgo and Gornon turned to the double and looked back at Smitty in realization.

"Two Rojbors?" gasped the alien commander.

"No, Gornon," said Rojbor grimly. "I am the true Rojbor and your madness ends here."

Mark was so shocked he stopped strangling Smitty and they both looked in awe. The window in the ship continued to crack and split, sucking out bigger pieces of the ship.

"Ten years ago, I discovered your genetic replication program, so I attempted to purge myself of it and you forever. I split a duplicate of myself," explained Rojbor, gesturing to Smitty. "You are mostly comprised of the human DNA I absorbed from John Schmidt. Gornon's DNA program was weakened in you, while it came back even stronger in me."

"You mean," concluded Goda. "This is all your fault?"

"Yes, and now I'm here to pay for my mistake," admitted Rojbor.

"Well!" cried Gornon, clicking the mouse. "You're too late!"

In the Meadowlands, the Agent 007 theme played through every audio speaker and microphone in the stadium. Gornon's terrible fat men shook in their seats for a moment, then dissolved harmlessly in the spot they were sitting in.

"No!" cried Gornon in surprise. "He's switched the disc! You've destroyed everything!"

Urgo and Gornon lunged for Rojbor. He shot Urgo and he froze on the spot, but Gornon was fast enough to bat away the guns. The two Kaltherians were locked in a strange mortal combat. They morphed together in a twisting mass of hands, faces and arms. The remaining Kaltherians in the room began to lose their cohesion. Mark and Goda struggled with the door, slowly pushing it open so they could squeeze out. Smitty leapt to his feet to help his counterpart, but Coach's head popped out of the mass.

"There's an escape pod in the back of the ship," he instructed. "I'll hold him here, get out while you can."

"But, you'll be—-"

"If one of us lives, Smitty," he implored. "We all live."

"Smitty!" called Goda, trying to hold the door open. "C'mon!"

"Yeah, hurry up, dickhead," added Mark, still a little mad.

Smitty slipped through the crack, just as the door overpowered Goda and Mark. It slapped shut right after him. Outside, the ship was spiraling out of the control, while inside, the Kaltherian crew melted in agony. Gornon began to push Rojbor toward the ever widening crack in the hull, but suddenly, Victor's head popped up from the mass to help in the fight.

"No way, dude," insisted Victor.

A second head that looked like Victor, controlled by Gornon, popped up.

"Stop! You're killing us both!"

In another part of the ship, Mark, Goda and Smitty were looking for the escape pod.

"You know, that stunt could really make someone question their sexuality," insisted Mark. "You can't do the chick from *Something About Mary*, can you?"

"Find the friggin' pod!" snapped Goda, anxious to leave.

"That looks like an escape pod," said Smitty, ignoring him.

Goda bent down to open the door, until Smitty said, "No, wait, that's for garbage."

"No pressure, but we're going to die in a minute," quipped Mark.

Finally, Smitty spotted the escape pod, which was built from an old Apollo moon capsule.

"I think that's it," pointed Smitty.

Goda and Smitty opened the door and scrambled inside. Mark tapped his pinky. The last of his elongated fingernails popped off and down the hall. For a brief second, his eyes glowed green again.

"C'mon!" hurried Goda.

Just as Mark bent down to get in, a Kaltherian tentacle shot out of an air vent and pulled him away. The dripping, dying head of Gornon reformed.

"You..." he wheezed in astonishment. "No wonder... Never stood a chance... You have the power...the green death..."

"Wait a minute!" said Mark. "You know what the Stuff is?"

"You mean," smiled the alien devilishly. "You don't? Ah-ha-ha, ha, ha, ha, ha..."

Gornon's laugh became garbled as he fell apart. Smitty pulled Mark toward the escape pod.

"No, wait! He knows! He knows!"

AVAILABLE SUMMER 2001

THE
ADVENTURE
CONTINUES IN
Tony DiGerolamo's
THE FIX

THE
COMIC BOOK
SERIES

WRITTEN AND CREATED
BY
TONY DiGEROLAMO

PENCILED AND LETTERED
BY
BRENDON FRAIM

INKED AND GRAY TONES
BY
BRIAN FRAIM

MURPHY'S ◉ LORE:™

ISBN 1-890096-07-5 $14.00 US

TALES FROM BULFINCHE'S PUB

Patrick Thomas

See how it all started with Murphy & the rest of the gang. The orignal collection is back with 4 all new stories about leprechaun Paddy Moran's bar at the end of the rainbow, where Dionysus pours the drinks and Hercules watches the door. The name of the place is Bulfinche's Pub. It is a second home to the legends of our day and a beacon to troubled souls, all lead there by the simple magic of the rainbow. One never knows what will come in the door next: Armageddon, or a terrified man with no socks. Whatever happens, two things are certain ope and Happiness never die, and the first drink is always on the house.

"A MASTEPIECE. THE MUST READ OF THE YEAR." **-MURPHY'S MOM**

"I COULDN'T PUT IT DOWN. Murphy glued it to my hand."**-ROY G.BIV**, *parapelgic clown, patron*

"WORTH ITS WEIGHT IN GOLD, at least in trade paperback." **-PADDY MORAN**, *Leprechaun. Owner & Proprietor of Bulfinche's Pub*

"DEVILISHLY CLEVER." **-MATHEW**, *Angel on the lam. Dishwasher.*

FOOL'S DAY

Patrick Thomas

Murphy & the gang are back. This time it's April Fool's Day, the annual contest to determine the best trickster. Most of the regulars have headed for the hills, in an attempt to avoid trouble. Trouble comes calling anyway, and it's up to a handful of tricksters to face off Faerie royalty Mab and Oberon, not to mention the US Air Force, before they start a war that unleashes deadly Nuclear Magic™ on an unsuspecting Earth.

"I LAUGHED, I CRIED, I FELT HUMAN AGAIN. Not that that's a compliment by any stretch of the imagination."
-COYOTE, Native American Tricker god

"MORE FUN THAN A BARREL OF HUMANS. Even one going over Niagra Falls." **-SUN WUKONG**, The Monkey King

ISBN 1-890096-11-3 $14.00 US

DESTINY'S DOOR

Judith Tracy

**Here's to those that hope and pray.
Fate has led you here today.**

Have we the power to grant you this,

Search your heart and make one wish.

Click here to Enter

DESTINY'S DOOR

Judith Tracy

ISBN 1-890096-08-3 $14.00 US

Someone is attempting to break into Donald Thurman's computer. An accomplished hacker himself, Donald tries to trace the interloper -- but there is nothing to find. Not even an identifying cyber address, something that should be impossible. Impressed with the invisible hacker, he succeeds in making contact only to find he has discovered a new life form.

They are sentient beings who live in a computer environment and are searching for their creator. Donald becomes their mentor, their friend and their confidant. *They* even set up a website to help others, in order to prove themselves worthy of meeting the creator. But the world of infinite data grows smaller. Soon it becomes more of a prison than a home. *They* want to apply their newfound knowledge. *They* want to experience all life has to offer. *They* want out and unwittingly, Donald opens the door: *Destiny's Door.*

ISBN 1-890096-10-5 $29.95 US

WORLD TREE™:

A roleplaying game of species and civilization.

Bard Bloom and Victoria Borah Bloom.

Welcome to the World Tree! Its upper branches are fifty miles wide and thousands of miles long; city-states dot the landscape amongst the forests and fields on their flat tops. The Verticals, the sides of the world-branches, are wild and dangerous and full of monsters, and never more than twenty-five miles away from even the most civilized areas.

Filled with stories and advice from the inhabitants, this book gives you the detailed information about the World Tree and its prime cultures you'll need to play your own stories of intrigue and magic on the civilized frontier, together with a completely integrated rules system.

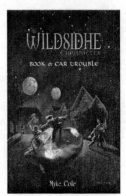

THE BEST OF
PIRATE WRITINGS
Tales Of Fantasy, Mystery & Science Fiction Vol. 1
Edited By Edward J. McFadden
Trade Paperback ISBN 1-89009604-0; US $12.95; 224 Pages
27 New Illustrations;
Limited Editions include:
100 Numbered Trade Paperbacks Signed By Editor $19.95 US
26 Lettered Hardcover Signed By Editor $75 US *ISBN 1-890096-06-7*

Christine Beckert - David Bischoff
Carroll Brown - Jack Cady
Jennifer B. Crow - Charles de Lint
Paul DiFilippo - Alan Dean Foster
Esther M. Friesner - Ed Gorman
Geoffrey A. Landis - Sharianne Lewitt
Ardath Mayhar - Edward J. McFadden III
- Bobbi Sinha-Morey - Leland Neville
Lyn Nichols - E. Jay O Connell
G.F. O Sullivan - Tom Piccirilli
Robert J. Randisi - Mike Resnick
Jessica Amanda Salmonson - A.J. Scott
Timothy S. Sedore - Eric Sonstroem
- Nancy Springer - Allen Steele - Sue Storm
and
Roger Zelazny
(One Of The Last Amber Stories)

PIRATE WRITINGS has been providing countless readers young and old, with cutting edge & traditional fiction since the winter of 1992.
THE BEST OF PIRATE WRITINGS
is a premiere collection of the very best of the magazine s tales featuring the talents of all the authors listed above.

Pirate Writings looks fabulous   quite an achievement ....
Dean R. Koontz

The contents [of *Pirate Writings*] are excellent.
Science Fiction Chronicle

"Sign on under the flag of McFadden's Jolly Roger now!"
Paul Di Filippo, **Asimov's**

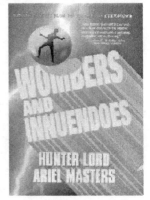

THE FIX:®
THE FIX IN OVERTIME
Tony DiGerolamo

The most powerful substance in the universe
The World's worst detective
The Earth will be invaded tonight and
the only guy who can save us
Still lives with his parents.

ISBN 1-890096-09-1 $14.00 US